Motion Pictures with Sound

Motion Pictures
With Sound

JAMES R. CAMERON

AUTHOR OF

Motion Picture Projection, Talking Movies,
Amateur Movie Craft, Electricity for the
Operator, Text Book on Radio, Motors and
Motor Generators, Etc., Etc.

LATE TECHNICAL EDITOR

Exhibitors' Trade Review, International Cinema
Review, Educational Film Magazine

CAMERON PUBLISHING COMPANY

MANHATTAN BEACH, N. Y.

ACKNOWLEDGMENT IS HEREBY MADE TO

WILLIAM FOX . . . . Fox Film Corp.

AARON FOX . . . . Fox Film Corp.

CORTLAND SMITH . . . . Fox-Case Corp.

E. I. SPONABLE . . . . Fox-Case Corp.

H. B. SANTEE . . . . . Electrical Research Products

T. L. DOWEY . . . . . . Electrical Research Products

CARL DREHER . . . . R. C. A. Photophone

E. E. BUCHER . . . . R. C. A. Photophone

A. G. HULAN . . . . R. C. A. Photophone

H. L. DANSON . . . . R. C. A. Photophone

WILLIAM H. BRISTOL . . . . . . Bristolphone Corp.

RAY K. IMMEL . . . University of Southern California

R. W. COTTON . . . . Samson Electric Co.

ANDREW J. McGREGOR . . . . Kliegl Bros.

P. A. McQUIRE . . . . International Projector Corp.

H. K. RANDALL . . . . Silver Marshall Inc.

KARL BRENKERT . . . . Brenkert Light Projection Co.

FRED C. GRISWOLD . . . . . Griswold Machine Works

J. H. McNABB . . . . Bell & Howell Co.

JOSEPH DUBRAY . . . . Bell & Howell Co.

DR. LEE DEFOREST . . . . Phonofilm

ACKNOWLEDGMENT IS HEREBY MADE TO

P. M. ABBOTT . . . . Motion Picture News

DONALD MACKENZIE . . . Bell Telephone Laboratories

WARNER BROS. . . . . Vitaphone

A. P. HOLLIS . . . . DeVry Corp.

L. D. STRONG . . . . . Essannay Manufacturing Co.

E. J. VALLEN . . . . Vallen Electric Co.

E. L. BRAGDON . . . . New York Sun

American Tel. and Tel. Co., U. S. Bureau of Standards, Messrs. Millikan and Gale, Messrs. Hopwood and Foster, Samuel Wein, American Cinematographer, Radio Engineering, Dr. Robert Burt, New York Times, Hoffman and Soons, The Society of Motion Picture Engineers

and all others who in any way assisted me with this work.

FOREWORD

THE success of sound pictures rests with you. The newest marvel of the era offers to you, who actually convey the audible screen entertainment to theatre patrons a challenge; your response will, to a great degree, determine the public's acceptance of sound-on-film.

So that you may better know what we have been striving for and what we have achieved in this new medium, I shall sketch briefly an outline of the part played by Fox-Case Corporation in the development of talking film.

The dream of such synchronization is as old as the motion picture itself. Almost twenty years ago the crude expedient of having persons speak from behind the screen was tried. Since that time innumerable methods, based upon this same idea of having light and sound originate from separate sources, have been worked out.

Always, progress along this line has been impeded by certain obstacles inherent in the method itself. Perfect synchronization of sound and action is difficult so long as each is produced separately. Moreover, recording of conversation and other sound effects is limited. It is necessary to confine such recording to sound-proof chambers, necessitating indoor photography and obviously precluding the use of genuine scenic backgrounds or the natural sounds of the great outdoors.

Several years ago we began experimenting with an entirely new method of synchronizing sound and action, which would permit the taking of pictures anywhere without special sound-proof enclosures, and which would also reproduce with perfect fidelity not only the human voice, but all other sounds of nature as well.

Whereas, previously sound effects had been reproduced phonographically—by the impressions made by sound waves on a wax record—the Fox Laboratories, working in collaboration with Theodore W. Case, scientist of Auburn, N. Y., applied themselves to the principle of recording sound photographically, using the ether waves for carriers much as radio does.

The advantage of this principle lay in the fact that light and sound could then be projected simultaneously from a single source, overcoming the difficulties of other methods which depended upon synchronizing a phonograph record of sounds with the action pictured on the screen. Moreover, since sound was to be recorded photographically instead of phonographically, it would be possible to make pictures anywhere, without the artificial limitations of special sound-proof chambers.

Several years of tireless experimentation and development along this line, at a cost of several million dollars, finally resulted in Fox Movietone. Art and science at last had found a perfect medium of expression, through which ideas could be conveyed instantaneously from mind to mind through ear and eye.

Fox Movietonews, which has won tremendous popularity with theatre managers and their audiences, was first introduced to the public on October 28, 1927. Its enthusiastic acceptance by the public has resulted in the increase from one to four weekly issues, supplied by 75 newsreel crews now photographing sound and action in every civilized country in North and South America, Europe, Africa and Asia.

By royal command Fox Movietone was selected as the method to pass on to posterity the voices and personalities of their Majesties George V, King of England and Alfonso XIII, King of Spain.

Fox Movietone is the miracle method of bringing to America—in all but the flesh—George Bernard Shaw. Movietone has acquainted us with the voices and mannerisms of President Coolidge, Colonel Lindbergh, Mussolini, Lloyd George, the Prince of Wales, Marshal Foch, Captain Fried and First Officer Manning, rescuers of the freighter Florida, Lady Astor, M. P., president-elect Herbert Hoover, ex-Governor Alfred E. Smith, Julius Rosenwald, internationally known millionaire philanthropist, and scores of world figures of equal prominence. A historic world event, the signing of the Kellogg Peace Pact, has been immortalized in Fox Movietone, whereby the scratching of the pen as President Coolidge and Secretary Kellogg affix their signatures, is made distinctly audible in the hush of the official chamber.

Now Movietone has graduated from fact to fiction— from life itself to the make-believe life of dramatic and comedy action. From short musical novelties and talking comedies which served to introduce to the public the voices and screen personalities of such entertainers as Raquel Meller, Gertrude Lawrence, Beatrice Lillie, Charles (Chic) Sale, Robert Benchley, Clark and McCullough and other celebrated thespians, Fox Movietone has evolved to the 100% dialog quality feature, "In Old Arizona." This superb, actionful love-drama filmed on a lavish scale against a sweeping background of Western desert and hills, established new records at the Roxy Theatre in New York and in the key cities where it enjoyed extended runs. "In Old Arizona" marked the attainment of full stature by the talking motion picture. Then followed "The Ghost Talks," a hilarious all-talking melodramatic farce wherein new thrills were added to spooky drama by means of Movietone.

The screen's first singing, dancing and talking comedy of the Old South, "Hearts in Dixie" with 200 entertainers from the levees and cotton fields marks another departure in audible film entertainment. Other dramatic highlights include such all-talking feature productions as "Speakeasy," "Thru Different Eyes," "The Valiant," "Behind That Curtain" and the first revue extravaganza of the sound films, "Fox Movietone Follies."

To insure a consistent supply of the finest grade of dialog pictures, we have opened recently Movietone City, the world's largest studio, comprising forty acres of land at Fox Hills, Westwood, California, especially designed and constructed for the production of sound pictures.

These achievements represent the culmination of five years of perfecting talking film and twenty-five years of motion picture production.

(Signed) WILLIAM FOX.

Fox Film Corp.,
New York City

Motion Pictures with Sound

I F THERE is any truth in that old bromide that the motion picture is still in its infancy, then within the last two years it has grown into a husky lunged youngster well able to talk for itself.

It may still slip up on its "S"s and its articulation may not be as clear and distinct as it might be, but we must all admit that the "silent drama" in this year of grace 1929 has at last found its voice.

The idea of the talking movie is by no means new, in fact it is as old as the moving picture itself, and much older than the moving picture as presented today. Dickson's first job with Edison away back in 1886 was to perfect a combination of Thomas E. Edison's new talking machine "with a practical zoetropie moving picture device." Since that time many and varied have been the methods used to synchronize the voice with the projected picture.

Since the birth of moving pictures there has always seemed to be something lacking with the screen presentation, to see pictures of persons talking or laughing, to see the firing of large guns, the falling of houses, to see great armies charging across the screen without hearing anything but the faint buzz of the projector has always left an impression of something missing.

Undoubtedly, it was due to this impression, that the old time piano-player was brought into the nickelodeons, remember how he had to memorize several selections and his job was to play some appropriate selection, or line from a song for each change of scene or action on the screen. Later the exhibitor went a step further and

11

engaged a couple of good talkers, whose job it was to stand behind the screen and speak the lines of the movie players and fill in their time between lines, rattling cocoa-nut shells on a marble slab, to imitate the sound of galloping horses, tooting automobiles horns, rattling pails of broken china, etc., etc., all to fit the action on the screen.

Long before the day of the Nickelodeon however, inventors were busy trying to perfect the "talking picture." In 1892 Demeny combined the voice and picture by means of his "Chronophotophone." This was a combination of a disc phonograph and a magic lantern and met with more or less of a success in Paris.

Two years later in 1894, Edison connected up his phonograph and his "Kinetoscope" and the combination was known as the "Kineophone." The "Kineophone" will be remembered as the "peep hole" projector into which the spectator looked. It was similar to those nickel-in-the slot machines found in the "penny arcades" of today. The music was supplied by the phonograph and the listener was obliged to use ear tubes. No attempt was made to synchronize the music and picture.

During the following five or six years there seems to have been a lull in "talking picture" activity, while inventors busied themselves with the "singing arc." In 1901 Ernst Ruhmer of Germany conducted a number of experiments with the "talking arc light."

The vital part of Ruhmer's apparatus was a selenium cell. Selenium is a substance varying in electrical resistance on exposure to light. Among the early investigators who endeavored practically to utilize this remarkable property was Alexander Graham Bell. In 1880 he devised his radiophone, in which a mica or glass diaphragm covered with a silvered foil was used to reflect a powerful beam of light upon a selenium cell placed in the focus of a silvered reflector. To the selenium cell were connected a pair of telephones and a battery. At the back of the silvered diaphragm was a flexible tube and mouthpiece into which words were spoken. The sound waves causing the diaphragm to vibrate sent pulsations of the reflected light upon the selenium cell, producing corresponding variations in its resistance and reproducing audible sounds in the telephone. Prof. Bell used this only over very short distances.

In 1898 Prof. H. T. Simon, of the University of Erlangen, discovered that an arc lamp the circuit of which was in proximity to a telephone circuit, was caused to vibrate very perceptibly. This suggested to him his interesting speaking arc by means of which he superimposed the sound waves produced by the telephone upon the circuit in which the arc was placed. He connected the lamp circuit with secondary winding of an induction coil, the primary circuit being connected with the carbon transmitter, and a battery. The sounds thus produced originally were very weak; but by employing a suitable carbon microphone, the sound was reproduced to large audiences.

Conversely, the arc could also be used in connection with telephone receivers to receive sounds.

Duddell, of England, had also made some most successful talking arcs. In his arrangement, in the secondary circuit, he placed a condenser, which prevents the lamp current's entering the induction coil, but allows the induction current in the transmitter circuit to pass without obstruction; and this arrangement had the effect of greatly increasing the sound.

Ruhmer had ingeniously combined the apparatus of

Bell, Simon, and Duddell and had successfully transmitted speech over a beam of light 4¼ miles in length. In his experiments he employed an arc lamp with a flaring arc 6 to 10 millimeters long, using an E. M. F. of 220 volts. The current varied from 4 to 5 amperes at 1 to 2 kilometers, 8 to 10 amperes for 3 to 4 kilometers, and 12 to 16 amperes for 5 to 7 kilometers, and the resistance of his selenium cell was 120,000 ohms in the dark, this falling to 600 ohms in full sunlight.

For the transmitting end, Ruhmer employed a carbon transmitter and a battery superimposing waves on the arc light circuit; and the beam of light was reflected to some distant point, where it was received by a parabolic reflector, in the focus of which is placed a selenium cell connected with a battery and a pair of very sensitive telephone receivers.

At the St. Louis Exposition, held in 1904, the American Telegraph & Telephone Company had an exhibit of the "Radiophone" and the following interesting description of same is from a little booklet issued to visitors to the fair.

The radiophone, which forms a part of the exhibit of the Bell Telephone Companies at the Louisiana Purchase Exposition, is the only practicable method of telephoning without the use of wires yet discovered. By its means the blinding rays of a searchlight may be made the path for human speech and other sounds. The rays of light will carry for miles every tone and inflection of the voice, the delicate shading and varying effects of orchestral music, every note and cadence of a song. With the help of the radiophone electric lights may be made to talk or be transformed into musical instruments. The radiophone is the embodiment of much that is wonderful in the transmission of sound, and it suggests the marvelous possibilities hidden in articles of common use. A bit of the black worsted which a woman uses in knitting, a tiny fragment torn from a silk dress, particles of rubber scraped with a pen knife from an old overshoe, these and many other substances may be made to repeat words flashed to them from an electric light miles away. So may the fine hairs found on the milkweed and the thistle-down which is the sport of the summer's breeze.

Alexander Graham Bell, the inventor of the telephone, also discovered the means by which wireless telephony has been made possible, and constructed the first apparatus to which the name of the radiophone was given. This was later perfected by an officer of the Bell Telephone system, and the wonderful results now attained are due to the scientific knowledge and skill of American inventors and engineers. In the experiments which led to the making of the radiophone Charles Sumner Taintor was associated with Professor Bell. They found that a great many substances could be made to give out sounds under the action of the heat carried in light rays of rapidly varying intensity. When light was thrown upon these substances they were, of course, subjected to the action of the heat in the rays, and it was to the heat that they responded. Changes in the degree of heat caused the substances to alternately expel and absorb gases. The gases set up motion in the air around them, and this motion took the form of sound waves. If the variations in the light rays and thus the changes in the degree of heat were controlled, it was possible to control the character of the reproduced sound. If the variations were produced by human speech, then the sound given out by the substances upon which the rays fell would repeat the spoken words. Fibrous material, dark in color, was found most susceptible to the action of heat. In other words, such every-day substances as lampblack, filings of rubber, worsted, silk, burnt cork, and blackened vegetable fibre could be made to talk. No human eye could detect the variations in the light ray, or measure the multitude of its vibrations. The bit of lamp-black or other substances gave the eye no hint of what was going on, yet it answered to each infinitesimal alteration in the heat waves traveling along the ray of light, the gases quivered about it, and sound waves sped on their course to the ears of the listener.

But there was another and even more wonderful means of employing a ray of light in the transmission of sound. In 1873, Mr. Willoughby Smith had demonstrated certain remarkable characteristics possessed by the element selenium. Professor Bell knew that under the influence of a ray of light of rapidly varying intensity, a bit of selenium, if placed in an electric circuit, would alter its resistance to the current as the light fluctuated. Here again it was evident that if the changes in the light rays were produced by the voice, the variations caused by the selenium in the electric current would correspond to the spoken words and through the medium of a telephone receiver could be transformed into exact reproductions of the tones of the speaker.

The first problem was to cause the sounds of the voice to produce fluctuations in the rays of light. Professor Bell accomplished this by the use of a very thin mirror. Fastened to the back of this mirror was a mouthpiece, and when words were spoken into the mouthpiece the mirror vibrated. The beam of light was thrown against the mirror, and then, by reflection, was directed to the receiving apparatus. As the mirror vibrated it caused fluctuations in the light rays, and corresponding variations in the degree of heat or the amount of light thrown upon the substance which reproduced the sounds of the voice. For instance, the word "Hello" spoken into the mouthpiece caused vibrations in the mirror. These in their turn caused fluctuations of the rays of light, and the receiving apparatus, under their influence, sent out sounds which reproduced the word.

Two forms of receivers were used by Professor Bell, and with each good results were obtained. In the simpler form no electric current was required. Vegetable fibre or lamp-black was placed in a glass bulb, from which rubber tubes similar to those used in old type phonographs extended to earpieces. The action of the rapidly varying degree of heat in the light rays caused the substances in the bulb to alternately expel and absorb gases. These gases in turn produced vibrations in the air in the tubes, and these vibrations made themselves felt upon the eardrums of the person who was listening, causing an exact reproduction of the words spoken at the transmitter. Receivers of this pattern were used when the radiophone was exhibited at the World's Columbian Exposition, at Chicago, in 1893. The light ray was thrown upon the mirror by an electric arc lamp. From the mirror the ray was deflected to the receiver placed in a reflector 100 feet distant. The rubber tubes from the glass bulb of the receiver were carried into a booth, and here the listener heard the words spoken into the mouthpiece attached to the mirror, 100 feet away.

Professor Bell also made use of a receiving device in which selenium was placed in an electric current with a telephone receiver. It is worthy of notice that the selenium receiver used by Professor Bell was of the type employed in the perfected radiophone of today. (1904.) Improvements have been made in methods of manufacture and the choice of materials, but no radical changes have been made.

With the radiophone as Professor Bell devised it, speech could be transmitted with distinctness for a distance of 600 or 700 feet, and for a number of years nothing was done to perfect the process. In 1896, Hammond V. Hayes, one of the engineers of the American Telephone and Telegraph Company, continued the work of experiment, and in his researches an arc light was used. In April, 1897, Hayes' assistant, E. R. Cram, noticed that a humming sound, audible in the receiver of the radiophone, corresponded in pitch with that produced by the generator supplying the current for the arc lamp used in the experiments. This discovery indicated that the arc light was peculiarly sensitive to slight variations in the electric current employed, and that the receiver of the radiophone was so sensitive to the light or heat variations in the arc as to render their fluctuations audible.

Starting with this discovery as a basis, Hayes concluded that if the words spoken into a telephone were made to act directly upon the electric lighting current, it would not be necessary to use the mirror employed by Professor Bell, and the distances which speech could be transmitted would be greatly increased. In the language of the electricians, the telephone current was superposed upon the lighting current. This was done by attaching the telephone wires to the wires in the arc lamp. When words were spoken into the telephone transmitter there was a variation in the

telephone current, and this variation was imparted to
the lighting current. More than that, the result was
to greatly magnify the effect of the telephone current,
when it was superposed upon the other, and the changes
in the light rays were thus of such intensity that speech
could be transmitted for distances which at first seem
incredible.

The use of a mirror in the radiophone was at best
not satisfactory. It was hard to obtain a mirror so thin

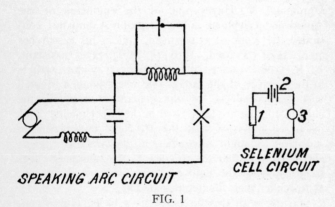

SPEAKING ARC CIRCUIT

SELENIUM
CELL CIRCUIT

FIG. 1

that it would respond to the words spoken into the
mouthpiece, and there was a diffusion of the light which
added to the difficulty of producing distinct sounds in
the receiver. With the early transmitting device
sounds could be sent only a few hundred feet. Today,
(1904), thanks to the discovery of the means by which
the telephone current is made to act upon the lighting
current, miles instead of feet measure the distance
which sounds may be transmitted. Application for a

patent embodying these discoveries was filed June 1, 1897, and the patent records show that not only was the radiophone originally invented in this country but that it was perfected by an American. In experiments made under the direction of Hayes, the sound of the voice has been heard with distinctness at points several miles from the transmitter, and it is known that good results might have been attained at much greater distances.

The investigations of Hayes resulted in the discovery of no new principle in the receiving apparatus, but it was improved in construction and the selection of materials. The receiver used today (1904) consists of a selenium cell enclosed in a glass bulb no bigger than that in which the homeopathic physician carries his pills. In making the cell, very fine brass wires are wound upon a bit of Indian pipe stone. The wires are then covered with a thin layer of selenium, and are attached to the wires which connect with the telephone receiver. The glass bulb is placed in a reflector which concentrates the rays of the lamp upon the selenium.

The apparatus is simple in appearance. At the point where the words are spoken into the radiophone there is a search-light like that used upon vessels. From the telephone transmitter, which is of special construction, wires lead to the lamp, and are attached to the wires which carry the lighting current. At a point which may be miles away is the reflector in which is placed the little glass bulb containing the selenium cell. From the bulb run wires which are connected with the telephone receiver. When words are spoken into the transmitter, the rays of the searchlight fluctuate, standing by the lamp, an observer sees no change in the intensity of its blinding glare, but if the beam is photographed it will be found when the plate is developed that the alterations due to the spoken words have been recorded by the sensitive film on the photographic plate. At the receiving station, the selenium responds to these fluctuations in the light rays, and the current in the wires there increases and diminishes in thousands of infinitesimal changes which reproduce not only the spoken words but the very tones of the voice of the speaker.

Investigations in connection with the radiophone developed another of its wonderful possibilities. It was found that an electric arc lamp is in itself a telephone receiver. The big light which hangs from a pole on the street corner may be made to talk. From the carbons in a lighted arc lamp there arises a column of vapor. If the lighting current is varied by superposing upon it a telephone current, the column of vapor around the carbons in the lamp will fluctuate and sound waves corresponding to the words spoken into the telephone will be given out. Music may be similarly sent through the arc lamp; the notes of a bugle coming clear and distinct from an ordinary electric light when no bugler is in sight afford a striking illustration of what may be done with the radiophone in this way. In Hayes' experiments, this means of showing the way in which an arc light may be turned into a musical instrument has often been employed.

The radiophone as yet has not been made of practical use. It is interesting as another illustration of the wonders of the electrical transmission of speech, and as such has attracted the attention of scientists the world over. Various means for its employment have been suggested. Vessels equipped with searchlight and telephone apparatus could by means of the radiophone talk together when long distances apart. In such a case a telephone transmitter on each vessel would be connected with a searchlight in the manner already described, and there would also be on each ship telephone receivers connected with selenium cells in large, curved reflectors. Words spoken on one vessel would travel along the rays of the searchlight to be picked up by the selenium cell in the reflector on the other ship. Words spoken there would similarly flit over the beam of the searchlight on that vessel to be heard in the telephone receiver on the other. It would not be necessary for the speaker on either ship to go to the searchlight. The telephone instrument might be in the captain's cabin or in any other part of the vessel. In the same way a vessel passing near the shore could communicate with persons on land, provided there was a radiophone so placed that the rays of its searchlight could be sent out over the water.

Perhaps the possibility of the giving of concerts by radiophone will appeal more strongly to the general public than the prospect of its use on shipboard. The music of a band playing in an electric light station could be heard wherever there was an incandescent light in the system radiating from the station. If a telephone transmitter were connected with the generating machinery, every note played by the band would cause a fluctuation in the electric current which, while not apparent to the eye, would be felt in every light in the system. If radiophone receivers were placed near these lights the selenium cells would respond to the variations in the current, and from the telephone receiver would come clear and distinct the music of the band. At the same time every arc lamp might be made to give out the sounds without the use of a receiver.

When a man first hears of the use of a searchlight as part of the radiophone, it may occur to him that the apparatus is capable of use only in the night time. But, as a matter of fact, as the rays of the sun are utilized for spelling out messages over long distances by means of the heliograph, so the rays of the searchlight may be used in the radiophone during the day. The radiophone, however, has one foe. Fogs and mist will prevent the transmission of messages by its means.

Hartmann's Improvements. In 1905 R. W. Hartmann made certain improvements on the "Photophone," which was the name given by Bell in 1880 to his invention of the "singing arc light," and which name is used today by the R. C. A. for their sound picture equipment system.

The objects of the improvement were first, to provide an elliptic mirror with a plane mirror covering it and having a narrow circular central hole; second, to provide a source of light in the focal point of the elliptic mirror; third, to provide a mouthpiece at a convenient angle to the axis of the elliptic mirror, its membrane being adapted to serve as a mirror for reflecting the pencil of rays of light from the elliptic mirror; fourth, to provide a sending tube similar to an astronomical telescope and adapted for changing the pencil of rays reflected from the membrane to a beam of nearly parallel rays which pass through the space, all the parts hitherto named forming the sender of a photophone; fifth, to provide a receiving tube having at the rear end a bottom and at the front end an object glass adapted to bend a beam of rays to the center; sixth, to provide in the bottom of the receiving tube a longitudinally movable small camera obscura having a narrow circular central hole in the focal point of the object glass; seventh, to provide within the small camera obscura a selenium cell or radiophone, and, eighth, to provide a circuit connecting the selenium cell or radiophone with a telephone.

Referring to the illustration, Fig. 2, it will be noted

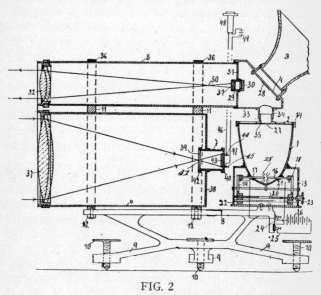

FIG. 2

HARTMANN'S PHOTOPHONE

that the sender is composed of an elliptic mirror (1), a plane mirror (2), a mouthpiece (3), with the membrane (4), and a sending tube (5). The receiver is composed of a receiving tube (6) and a small camera obscura (7). All the parts are shown as combined and supported by a table (8) provided with, preferably, three feet and adjusting screws. The two tubes are parallel to each other and may be superposed and rigidly conected in any known and approved manner. The plane mirror (2) is provided with a narrow circular hole (27) in the axis of the elliptic mirror (1). For producing the rays of light within the elliptic mirror any convenient source of light may be employed. An arc light (15) is used in the arrangement illustrated. Means are provided so that by turning the wheel (23) the two carbons can be simultaneously and longitudinally shifted in opposite directions, striking the arc. The arc light is caused to remain in the focus of the elliptic mirror (1).

At (43) a selenium cell or radiophone of any known construction is secured. This selenium cell is shown as consisting of a ceramic plate and a zigzagged selenium wire embedded in the surface of this plate. The two ends of this zigzagged selenium wire are connected with two binding posts, and the latter by two wires with a telephone (48) and a battery (49), whereby a circuit is formed. The telephone (48) is not shown in the proper size, but merely diagrammatically, as its construction is immaterial for the present.

The photophone described is operated in the following manner: It is directed toward the respective receiving station. After striking the arc this arc will emit rays of light in all directions; but only the rays in the axis of the elliptic mirror (1) and those very little deviating therefrom will be able to at once pass through the narrow circular hole (27) in the plane mirror (2). Thereby an intensive thin and very acute-angled pencil of rays of light is produced, which can easily be subjected to strong variations of the intensity.

The pencil of rays of light passing through the central hole (27) strikes the mirror (28) and is therefrom deflected to the lens (30). The beam of parallel rays passing from the lens (30) to the other lens (31) converges to the focus (50), and thence diverges to the large lens (32), from which nearly parallel rays of light pass through the space, so that this beam is capable of producing an image in a telescope at a distant station. Of course, the receiving tube is made sufficiently large in diameter for receiving the full image. When assuming the tube (6) to be at the receiving station and its lens (37) to receive the beam of rays from the lens (32) of the sending station, the rays be bent toward the center and made to converge to the focus—i.e., the central hole (41) in the cover (39)—after which they will diverge and produce the image on the face of the selenium cell (43) or radiophone.

When the operator talks immediately in front of the mouthpiece (3), the membrane (4), and with it the mirror (28), will be thrown into a complicated state of vibration, which represents the three elements of the speaker's voice—namely, pitch, intensity and quality. The pencil of rays of light will, of course, be subjected to these vibrations by the mirror (28), and these vibrations will be transmitted with the rays through the space to the lens (37) of the distant receiving tube (6) and produce variations in the resistance of the selenium cell (43) or radiophone. The currents circulating in the circuit (46) (47) of the battery (49) and the telephone (48) will register all the peculiarities of the speaker's voice and produce changes in the magnetism of the magnet and of the membrane of the telephone (48). The operator at the distant receiving station placing his ear to the membrane of the telephone (48) will therefore hear the very sounds given out by the speaker at the sending station.

Recording Voice on Film. Until this time (1905), the "singing arc light" or "talking arc light" had been used for voice transmission only. Ruhmer now began his experimentation in using the arc light for recording the voice upon a sensitized photographic film. He passed the sensitive film rapidly before a narrow slit through which the light of the flame could strike it. The slit was about $\frac{1}{16}$ of an inch in width and of such a length as to admit of the seeing of both the carbon points through it when the eye was in the position of the photographic film. With this apparatus he succeeded in getting records which were sufficient to satisfy him that the vibrations of the flame were recorded, but the record was not sharply enough defined to admit of reproduction.

By substituting for the slotted metal a cylindrically ground lens this difficulty was overcome. It is the property of a lens of this character to produce at its focus an image which is not at all reduced in size lengthwise of the lens, but which is reduced to the mere thickness of a line in the other direction.

Placing the cylindrically ground lens with its axis across the line of motion on a long photographic film, the vibrating light of the speaking flame was thrown upon it. With proper motive apparatus the film was moved rapidly in front of the lens. The result was a record formed in lines so fine as to repeat distinctly practically every vibration of the voice of the speaker. The film having been developed and fixed forms a record which can be retailed indefinitely. The reproduction of the voice from this record is accomplished by a reversal of the process by which the record was produced.

To make the record talk it is again mounted upon its rollers and wound from one to the other so as to be passed rapidly in front of the light of an arc lamp. The light passing through it falls upon a selenium cell and this in the manner already described changes its variations into vibrations on the disc of a microphone.

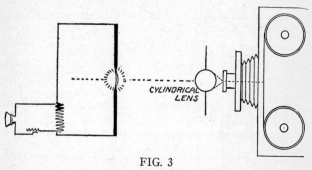

FIG. 3

MAKING A VOICE RECORD BY MEANS OF THE SPEAKING ARC AND PHOTOGRAPHY

We now come to the period when attention was given to the synchronizing of the voice with the picture.

Synchronizing Voice With Picture. The production of imitation sounds or effects is quite a different problem to the reproduction of the actual sounds themselves. In the latter case the sound record has to be made and reproduced with the picture. It must, moreover, keep in time with the picture; that is to say, there must be "synchronism" between the sound and the picture records. The ordinary victrola record is obtained by the action of a vibrating membrane which produces a series of indentations in a soft surface of wax.   These indentations are used to reproduce the vibrations of a membrane, and thereby reproduce the original sounds.   Stripped of all refinements, this is the essential principle of the victrola.   If, then, a record of the sounds can be made simultaneously with the photographic record, it would not at first sight appear

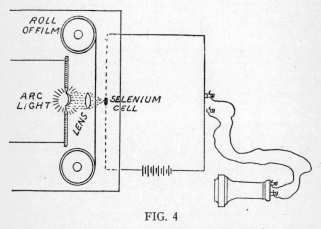

FIG. 4

REPRODUCING THE VOICE FROM THE PHOTOGRAPHIC RECORD

to be difficult to reproduce them in synchronism.   The first of these problems is rendered difficult by reason of the limitations of the sentiveness of the recording victrola.   The recording instrument must be within a certain range of the sounds, and for a speaker or actor the range is not a large one, and it is difficult to get the instrument near enough and keep it outside the picture view. Accordingly another method has been resorted to, which is applicable in a large number of cases. The music record is taken first, and the picture film is produced to the accompaniment of the record. To succeed with this method it is obviously essential that the speaking, singing or acting should synchronize with the sound record for synchronism between the same return and the picture film to be possible. A further limitation arises from the size of record obtainable. A small or short record means a short film. The size and length of an ordinary record is very limited, and for a speech, sketch or piece of any material length, several records are necessary, and these would need to follow on at the proper time. Having obtained the record and picture film, the problem of reproducing them synchronously is still a formidable one. It is, of course, theoretically possible for the projectionist to keep his eye on the screen and his ear on the victrola, and to control the projector or victrola so as to maintain synchronism. This, however, throws an additional resposibility on the already over-burdened projectionist, and is not a practicable method. Accordingly, either an auxiliary device is necessary to automatically indicate to the projectionist if the synchronism is being maintained, or some means by which the running of the projector or victrola, or both, is automatically adjusted to maintain synchronism.

In one of Gaumont's earliest methods, introduced in 1902, a motor was used to drive the projector. This motor was electrically controlled from the victrola. The victrola drives a shaft, carrying collector rings, of an electric circuit; and carrying also rotating brushes, which rub on a divided collector, the sections of which are connected to the stator of the motor. The next step in advance is the use of synchronized motors for driving both the victrola and the projector. Mester, in Germany, appeared to have been working on these lines, and special types of motors were used. The two motors of identical design and the same power were driven from the same current, and in order to better maintain synchronism the motor armatures each had a number of sections which were connected in pairs. A switchboard near the projector included a starting switch, whereby the victrola was first set in motion; and when the record commences, the disc operates a switch to start the projector. A voltmeter on the switchboard indicated any want of synchronism which was corrected by accelerating or retarding the projector. This is effected by coupling the projector with its driving motor through a differential gearing, which was operated from a separate motor. This latter motor was started by an auxiliary two-way switch, so that the differential could be used to retard or accelerate the projector to restore the synchronism. The results obtained with the Chronophone were extremely satisfactory, and by the use of the Auxetophone, in which the sound was intensified by means of compressed air, the possibility of the Chronophone in large halls was looked upon as a possibility, as was evidenced by its use at the old Hippodrome in Paris, which had a seating capacity of over four thousand.

The use of indicators for automatically indicating to the operator any want of synchronism has been adopted by many inventors in various ways. In one of the earliest, two indicating elements were used, one consisting of a disc, rotated directly from the projector and the other a concentric pointer, rotated by an electromagnet, which is intermittently energized by a circuit,

completed on every revolution of the victrola spindle
by means of a cam on the spindle. The disc carries a
mark, and so long as the mark on the disc and the
pointer are coincident, synchronism is being maintained.
If the pointer leads or lags, the projector is speeded up
or slowed down accordingly to restore synchronism.

There is undoubtedly a comparative simplicity in such
a method as this, of which there have been many varie-
ties. In one by Thomasin, a pointer is rotated intermittently by a pawl and an electro-magnet energized
from the shaft of the victrola. The electrical escape-
ment is mounted on a coaxial disc which is rotated in the
opposite direction from the projector shaft. So long
as synchronism is maintained there will be no movement of the pointer, and any movement of the pointer
indicates the adjustment necessary for the projector.
With this apparatus there is a single indicating element
only.

Another apparatus of this type was the Vivaphone,
devised by Hepworth, in London. In this instrument
a wheel, B, Fig. 5 carrying the indicating pointer M,
is rotated by two pawls, D, I, which are actuated by
two electro-magnets, G, L. These electro-magnets are
intermittently energized from the projector and victrola
respectively. The spindle B^1 of the wheel B rests
between parallel bars, A^3, and if synchronism is upset,
one pawl will rotate the wheel more quickly than the
other one, and thereby cause the pointer M to move
to one side or the other. The pointer carries two red
and green discs, M^1, M^2, which are thus brought opposite the lamp, and indicate any disturbance of synchronism. The attractiveness of the Vivaphone is that it is
adaptable for any victrola and any projector. The
make and break contacts for intermittently energizing

the electro-magnets are carried on two fittings, *S. T*, Figs. 6-7. The fitting *S* rests on the disc, and has a knife-edge engaging in the slot of the centre pin, and the fitting *T* is carried by the driving shaft of the projector respectively.

Another somewhat different method and apparatus, invented by Mr. Jeapes, which bears the stamp of extreme simplicity, was brought out as the Cinephone

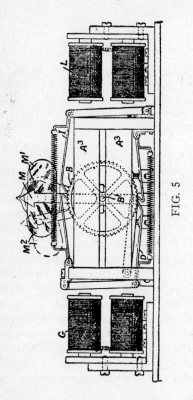

FIG. 5

by the Warwick Trading Company. In this method a rotating pointer is attached to the victrola and driven by it. The victrola is positioned so that a record of the rotation of the pointer is produced on the film at one corner thereof. The victrola is placed near the corner of the projection screen, on which the reproduction of the pointer appears. The projectionist then controls the projector so that the reproduction maintains the same angular speed as the pointer.

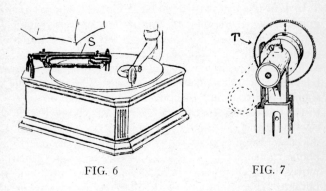

FIG. 6   FIG. 7

A difficulty with several synchronizing devices where an indicating pointer is used arises when a film breaks or is damaged, and a section of it has to be cut away. In such cases it is necessary to slow down the projector until the victrola catches up, but there is no visible indication when synchronism is restored. With the Cinephone, however, the restoration of synchronism is indicated by the reproduction of the pointer on the screen.

In another type of device, by Count Proszynski, the

projector is coupled with the victrola by connecting a spindle of the projector with an air-pump, the air outlet of which is regulated from the phonograph in such a manner that when synchronism is faulty the bellows actuate a brake or otherwise control the speed of the projector.

Lauste's Method. In another and altogether different system, invented by Mr. Lauste in 1906, the sound as well as the picture are simultaneously recorded on the film.

In Lauste's method the sound record is made photographically. A microphone transmitter, such as is used for collecting the sound-waves at concert halls for transmission, or alternatively, one or more horns or trumpets, *a*, Fig. 8, connecting with any ordinary loud-sounding telephone or microphone transmitter, *b*, receives the sounds, and transmits them over an electric circuit, *c*, *d*, to the receiver in the camera, *A*. At the receiver is an electro-magnet, *B*, and the varying electric currents produced by the action of the sound-waves in the microphone transmitter *b*, vibrate a slotted diaphragm which moves between a fixed light and a fixed slotted diaphragm. The vibrations of the diaphragm corresponding to the sound-waves produce variations in the light openings through the diaphragms and consequently variations in the intensity of light falling on the sensitive film *m*, behind the diaphragm are produced. The sensitive strip on which the light falls, is adjacent to the picture area of the film and, when developed, forms the sound record. The sound record must be made while the film is moving continuously, before or after it is fed intermittently through the gate *T* of the camera. It will thus be seen that the sound record on the film is a few picture lengths behind the corresponding section of the picture record. To reproduce the sound record, use is made of the fact that the resistance or conduc-

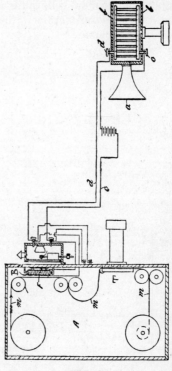

FIG. 8

tivity of a selenium cell, when included in an electric circuit, b, varies in accordance with the intensity of light acting on it. In the projector, Fig. 9, the film passes between a lamp, p', and a selenium cell, r, in circuit with a loud-sounding microphone or telephone, H. The variations in the current produced by the variations in the light intensity transmitted through the sound record o, and falling on the selenium cell, cause a corresponding variation of the sound membrane in the loud-sounding microphone or telephone, H.

In another method, by Mrs. Von Madeler, the sound

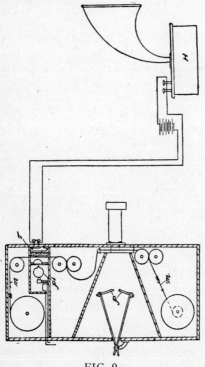

FIG. 9

record on the film is constituted by a wary edge produced on the film. The sound box of the victrola has
to be actuated in proximity to the film. The styles consists of a rotated cutter mounted on a pivoted bracket
and vibrated by an arm, connected with the diaphragm
of the sound box. The cutter is adjacent to the edge
of the film and the sound-waves are thus recorded and
represented by the wavy edge of the film produced by
the cutter. As in the previous case, the sound record
is taken while the film runs continuously, either before
or after the film is fed intermittently through the gate.
A duplicate record may be simultaneously reproduced
on the other edge of the film. To reproduce the sound
record the sapphire or needle of the victrola sound box
has a flat end resting against the edge of the film as it
passes through the projector. The pressure of the
needle is regulated by a balance weight. An alternative
to the method of cutting the edge of the film by a rotary cutter consists in heating a platinum wire to a dull
red heat sufficient to burn the edge of the film, and
mounting this wire on an arm or frame connected with
the diaphragm of the sound box, so that the vibrations
of the wire may burn to a variable depth along the edges
of the film. This method may be used to produce a
film sound record of an ordinary disc record. With the
above method the victrola must obviously be near the
camera and the projector, whereas by the photographic
or photo-electric method the victrola can be anywhere
both in recording and reproducing. It is possible to use
more than one victrola, which is Rosenberg's method,
devised more especially to compensate for the disturbing effect on the sound production due to the movement
of the source of sound—say a speaker or actor. This
dependency of the sound received, upon the movement

and distance of the sound, is well instanced by the sound of a whistle of an approaching and passing train. To produce a more correct sound reproduction two microphones are used to produce a sound record on a film running at one side of the picture film. For reproduction, two sound-reproducing devices are put on either side of the screen. The films, both in the camera and projector, can be run from the same gearing, and the synchronism can be adjusted by having a movable gate carrying the sound-reproducing devices. A further advantage of having a reproducer on either side of the stage is that the sound appears to come from the correct side of the picture.

Between the years 1906 and 1912 there seems to have been another lull in sound picture activities, but in the years 1912-1913 many applications were made for patents pertaining to sound pictures and sound picture equipment.

In June 1912 C. E. Fritts applied for a patent covering an invention relating to recording variations or pulsations in sounds, light or electric currents in a permanent or tangible form and reproducing same at will not merely at the instrument alone but also at any other instrument suitably connected therewith (1,213,613).

In May 1913 Elias Ries submitted his sound record method and method of reproducing photographic sound records. The invention for the sound recording method relates to methods for the production of photographic records of sounds, whether vocal, musical or of other character, and of type such that the original sound can be accurately reproduced therefrom with facility. The invention, although in certain broader aspects thereof applicable to the preparation of sound records alone, has its preferred application to the production of talking picture film record, that is, to moving picture films bearing a succession of photographs of successive stages in the action, and taken in usual manner, and provided with one or more continuous sound records laterally of the picture, which represent the amplitudes and phases of vibrations of the sonorous action, such as music, speech or the like, occurring and recorded simultaneously with the visual action.

The sound record is produced by causing undulatory variations in light intensity similar in form to the vibrations of the air accompanying the sonorous action, and subjecting narrow portions of the film in rapid succession to the influence of the varying light. The source of light is preferably a tungsten or other metal filament lamp of small power, although an arc lamp may be used, and the variations are imposed preferably by the well-known singing arc principle, in which the sound vibrations act upon a microphone, which automatically varies resistance in circuit with the lamp, in conformity with the sound vibrations, and effects synchronously therewith, undulatory variations in the light intensity. The exposure of the film to the varying light at any moment is limited to a portion definitely restricted in the direction lengthwise of the film, by moving the photographic film or other sensitized surface in close proximity or contact with an opaque screen having a very small aperture. This aperture or window is preferably in the form of a narrow slit, and is of much greater width than length, the width being governed by the available space on the photographic film outside of the usual sprocket holes or between the line of pictures and the sprocket holes when the sound record is to form part of a motion picture. For sound records only, the width of the aperture may be much greater, if desired; but the length, that is the dimension taken lengthwise of the sound record, should always be proportional to the length of the shortest sound waves to be recorded. By moving the photographic film or other sensitized surface in close contact with the perforated screen, the exposed area of the sensitized surface is definitely fixed under all conditions of light, and all diffusion of light beyond the area of the aperture is prevented so far as possible. It is preferred, moreover, to focus the light from the lamp in a pointed or conical pencil directed upon the window opening, as by the use of an appropriate spherical lens. The film is moved preferably at a uniform rate past the window aperture or slit, in photographing the sonorous action, at a speed such as to differentiate the imprints of the denser and more attenuated parts of the sound waves photographed seriatim, the period of photographic exposure being so related to the speed of the record and to the duration of said portions of sound waves as to prevent blurring or overlapping. By the combined use of the photographic film moving in close contact with the screen having the small window aperture and the focusing lens, the light from the lamp acts uniformly over the exposed part of the film, so that sharper variations in light intensity are imposed upon the successively exposed parts of the film, producing more distinct and more substantial differentiations in translucency of the developed film for better sound reproduction than if the light were more widely diffused over the film.

This is particularly true where a small power tungsten filament or equivalent lamp is employed, operating at substantially rated current consumption, where the candle power will vary relatively widely with the relatively small increments or decrements of current due to the operation upon the microphone of the air waves accompanying the vocal or other sound.

In the preferred application to talking pictures, in which the sound record is photographed concurrently with the taking of the pictures, and upon a strip or border of the film laterally of the pictures, the rate of film advance is limited by the exigencies of moving picture requirements to a speed in the order of about one foot per second. As the sound records, unlike the visual records, should be substantially continuous, rather than discreet, they cannot be conveniently produced on the intermittently moving film, and are consequently recorded at a portion of the film beyond the shutter opening of the picture taking lens, that is, at a region where the film moves at uniform speed. In this application, the length of film momentarily exposed is highly restricted, being of a length in the order of that of a small pin hole, which length is traversed by the film, even at the relatively slow speed of moving picture operation, in the minute interval of a fraction of a sound wave.

Referring now to Fig. 10, the film 1 in its downward travel through casing 2, passes in succession over the upper guide roll 7, upper positively-driven feed sprocket or drum 8, and its guide roller 9, by the action of which the film is unwound at a uniform rate of speed from the upper reel (not shown) and is caused to form the upper loop 18. The film then passes between the upper intermittent sprocket 10 and its guide roller 11, down between the lower intermittent sprocket 12 and its guide roller 13, and forming the lower loop 20, thence between lower positively-driven sprocket 14 and its guide roller 15, thence downward in a vertical line under the guide roller 16 and over the guide roller 17, from which it is wound onto the lower film reel 4.

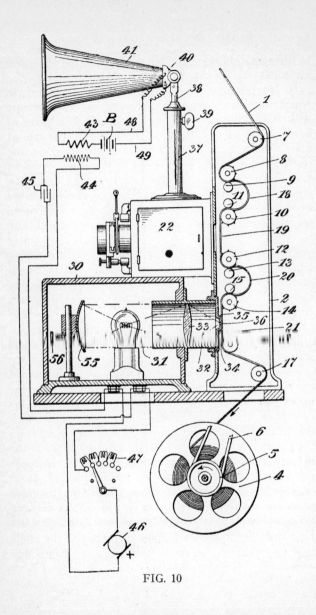

FIG. 10

It will be observed that in addition to the two loops 18 and 20, the film in its passage, forms two vertical face sections 19 and 21, each approximately a trifle longer than the width of a single picture. The lower vertical film section 21 is in the focal plane of the sound camera 30. The upper section is in the focal plane of the lens (not shown) of a moving picture camera 22 of any suitable construction, which exposes the central portion of the film. The edge portion or portions of the film on which the photographic sound record is to be received are shielded from the light and are thus left unexposed during the transit of the film behind the shutter-opening of the picture-taking lens, which is preferably located, as shown, a short distance above the sound camera 30.

This sound camera consists of a casing containing an independent source of light, which may be a small tungsten or other metal-filament incandescent electric lamp 31 capable of being operated at a high degree of incandescence, although an electric arc lamp or any other suitable source of light may be used, if desired. Behind the lamp is mounted a standard 54 carrying an adjustment reflector 55 which may be secured upon the standard by the thumbscrew 56. The light of the lamp direct or reflected is thrown, as shown, by dotted lines, upon a spherical lens 33 in a tube 32 in the front of the casing 30. The tube is closed at its forward end by an adjustable cap-piece 34 having a raised central portion 35 pierced with either a narrow slit 36 or a small round or square pin hole opening 36', said cap-pieces being preferably interchangeable. The moving film 1 travels downward in close proximity to the raised portion 35 and with that portion of its surface on which the sound is to be recorded, for instance, lateral strip or border 50 directly in front of the light opening 36.

Mounted at the upper rear portion of the apparatus is shown a standard 37 containing an adjustable sliding rod 38, that may be extended and turned to any position and locked against displacement by wing nut 39. The upper end of rod 37 has a swivel joint into which is clamped a telephone transmitter or microphone 40, which is provided with a large tapering horn or megaphone 41, designed and adapted to collect the atmospheric sound waves and to direct and focus them upon the diaphragm of the transmitter 40. The minimum height of the horn 41 when the device illustrated in Fig. 10 is used in connection with a portable motion picture camera, is such that the entire camera mechanism, including the casing 30 containing the photophonic recording appliances, may be mounted as a single, self-contained unit below the line of swing of the horn. The sound receiving horn 41, may, however, be located at any convenient point either alongside of the camera or at any desired or suitable distance from the scene and sounds, to be photographed.

The transmitter 40, whether mounted on the apparatus or located at a distance therefrom, is in electrical circuit through the line wires 48 and 49, with a battery B in series with the primary winding 43 of an induction coil, whose secondary winding 44 is in series with a condenser 45 and with the terminals of the lamp 31, as shown. All of these devices in practice, are preferably included within the casing 30 or other enclosed portion of the apparatus. The terminals of the lamp 31 are likewise independently connected in the usual manner, by means of the circuit wires shown, with a suitable source of direct current, such as the generator 46, the voltage of which is regulated by rheostat 47.

In the operation of recording talking pictures, the visible phase of the performance or other occurrence combining visible and sonorous action, is recorded by the camera 22, in the usual manner for taking moving pictures. The horn 41 is disposed in appropriate relation to intercept the sound waves and the circuit of the lamp 31 is closed. The film moves intermittently between the rollers 10 and 12, taking moving pictures on the film section 19 in the regular manner, while the film section 21 moves past the pin hole or other narrow slit 36 in the sound recording camera, continuously at a uniform speed usually about one foot per second, that is, at the mean speed of the moving picture camera film. It will be understood that the film section 19 is covered and screened from the light over the entire section except that part of the film which is opposite the usual picture aperture or window, and that film section 21 is likewise covered or screened by screen 35 except the small part opposite the aperture 36, and that the film in passing across the said screen 35 is held in such close proximity thereto by the feeding mechanism, or otherwise, that the light rays passing through the aperture 36 will act only on the film area limited by the size of said aperture.

Specifically, the sound waves entering the horn 41 from a distant point are concentrated upon the diaphragm of the microphonic transmitter 40, forcibly vibrating the same to vary the resistance of the primary circuit, containing the battery B and the primary coil 43. The latter induces undulating or alternating currents of high tension corresponding in form and frequency with the sound waves impinging upon the diaphragm, in the secondary coil 44, which currents pass across the condenser 45, and become superposed upon the steady current flowing through the lamp 31 from the dynamo or other source 46. The direct current from the source 46, it will be seen, cannot jump across the condenser 45, nor affect the induction coil 43, so that the net result of the variable current impressed upon the lamp 31 by the action of the transmitter 40 will be alternately and rapidly to increase and decrease the intensity of the light in exact accordance with the original sound waves. More particularly, induction coil 43-44 inducing currents flowing alternately in opposite directions through the lamp filament, as the microphone resistance alternately increases and decreases, those currents that flow with the normal lamp current serve to reinforce it and augment the candle power, while those that flow against the normal lamp current oppose it and cause a diminution of the normal luminosity.

The light from the lamp 31 passes into the tube 32 and impinges upon the spherical lens 33, which effectively concentrates or focuses the light upon the screen 35 so that the light passing through the fixed minute aperture 36 will act uniformly over the area of the film exposed by the aperture. The light from the lamp is thus effectively concentrated at any instant upon the relatively minute film areas momentarily exposed. Since, moreover, both the candle power and the actinic effect of the ordinary tungsten or other equivalent lamp operating at rated current consumption, change markedly with small increments or decrements of current, it follows that the degree of exposure of the film will vary relatively widely with the relatively minute changes in lamp current, taking place synchronously with and proportionally to the varying amplitudes of sound or air vibration. Reis's invention for reproducing photo-

graphic sound records relates to the method and apparatus for making photographic records of sound by
causing the sounds that are to be recorded to produce
varying electrical impulses in an electric circuit which
in turn cause varying intensities of light for affecting
a photographic film. And more particularly it relates
to combined motion pictures and sound records photographed on the same film. Also to methods and apparatus for reproducing such sound records or combined
motion pictures and sound records.

To reproduce such a record, there is employed a
method in which light rays of constant luminosity are
projected through an apertured screen similar to the
screen employed in making the record, and the record
film is moved constantly at a uniform speed in such
relation to the aperture, that only an area equal to the
area of the aperture will be exposed to the light rays,
and the light rays passing through the record film of
varying opacity will be projected upon a light sensitive
cell or plate, such as selenium. This cell is connected
in an electric circuit connected with a sound reproducing device or telephone, and in accordance with the
variations in light rays passing through the record, the
light sensitive cell will produce variations in the resistance or cause varying impulses in said circuit to actuate
said sound reproducing device or telephone (1,607,-
480).

In June 1921 Josef Engl of Berlin submitted his
"photographic sound record reproducing means."

The invention relates to improvements in photographic sound record reproducing means, and more
particularly to means utilized in the reproduction of
sound which is recorded photographically on a sensitized film or other light-sensitive carrier.

In the system, such as is contemplated herein, sound is recorded by causing the sound waves, by means of a microphone or the like, to set up acoustically-modulated currents in a circuit, which includes the microphone. These acoustically-modulated currents serve to modulate the intensity of illumination of a source of light. Light from this source, varying in intensity in correspondence with the original sound waves, passes through a narrow slit and falls upon a moving sensitized film whereon the sound record is made in the form of narrow lines extending transversely upon the film. The varying intensity of the recording light causes photographic blackening of the film of varying densities.

When the film has been developed and a positive film made therefrom, the latter is run at the same speed between a constant source of light and a light-sensitive element, such as a photoelectric cell. The varying quantities of light which pass through the film will set up currents in the circuit of the photo cell, which currents correspond to the variations of light impinging upon the photo cell, as is well known.

The present invention has to do with the form of light source which is utilized in reproducing the photographic sound records such as have just been described and with means for insuring the constancy of the illumination from this light source. In accordance with the invention the central portion only of the luminous face of the positive electrode of an electric arc is used as the source of light which is to illuminate the moving sound record film. This central portion of the positive crater, as it is termed, of the arc-discharge, is of an unvarying brilliance regardless of variations of the current flowing across the arc. In accordance with the invention provisions are made such that the outer marginal portions of the positive crater surface, as well as the luminescent portion of the arc itself and the negative pole of the arc are screened off so that no light from these portions of the electric arc source will be able to illuminate the film.

An object of the invention consists in the provision of means for illuminating the film with a constant intensity of light in accordance with the foregoing.

It should be understood that photographic sound records may be made in the form of a succession of narrow lines extending transversely of the film, which lines are all of equal length but are of varying density or degree of blackening of the photographic emulsion so as to render the latter more or less opaque to the passage of light therethrough. That is the form of record particularly referred to above and which we prefer. A second form of record can likewise be used in connection with this invention, this being the form in which transversely extending record lines on the film are of varying lengths so that one edge of the sound record thus formed is bounded by a varying curve.

In the reproduction of photographic sound records, as contemplated herein, it is extremely important that the intensity of the light source employed should be made as strong as feasible and also that the same should be as constant as possible. The light should pass through a narrow slit and illuminate only one of the sound record lines on the film at a time, since if more than one such line is illuminated at a time the light passing through the film and falling upon the photo cell will correspond to more than one sound vibration and various sound frequencies thus will not be clearly reproduced. The width of the record line on the film which is thus to be illuminated may depend upon the rate of speed at which the film is progressed. The record line must be so narrow that at a given speed of travel of the film the vibrations of the highest sound frequencies which are to be recorded will be recorded singly and separately. The maximum audible sound frequency lies in the neighborhood of 10,000 vibrations per second. If the film travels at a speed 50 centimeters per second, for example, when sound of a frequency of 10,000 per second is to be recorded, each vibration corresponds to the product of 50 divided by 10,000 or 1/200ths of a centimeter of film. In other words, the sound record should be formed of transverse lines each having a width less than 1/200ths of a centimeter in order that frequencies of 10,000 per second may be recorded individually. If the film moves at a speed less than 50 centimeters per second, the width of the record lines should be correspondingly reduced.

Since the sound record lines should be so narrow it will be seen that the quantity of light passing through the film at any moment is small. It is, therefore, of extreme importance that the intensity of the luminous source should be strong.

Further the necessity of maintaining the reproducing light constant, if a faithful reproduction of the sound is to be secured, is made clear by the fact that every undesired change in the intensity of illumination of the reproducing light varies the current produced by the photo cell. The variations of current produced by the photo cell correspond to the variations of light which pass through the film and these should correspond only to variations of recorded sound. Any change in the intensity of light emitted by the light source varies the sound which is reproduced by the loud speaker or other sound reproducing device, which is operated by the current produced by the photo cell.   (1,608,261)

Transmitting, Recording, Reproducing Sound.   J. Tykocinski-Tykociner sent in his application for patent covering a "method of and means for transmitting, recording and reproducing sound."   This invention related to the same general subject matter as his prior application filed in June, 1922.

The present application discloses certain improvements and refinements of the apparatus for use in connection with the prior systems disclosed in said applications, and this application discloses among other things, certain specific improvements as follows: first, improvement in the recording camera and recording mechanism to make the recording of sound or variations of audio-frequency or radio-frequency more simple and accurate; second, improvement in the means for transforming vibrations or current variations to variations of light; third, improvement in the means for transforming sound vibrations into variations of current, familiarly termed the telephone transmitter.   (1,640,-557)

Another application filed in 1923 was by Theodore Willard Case of Auburn, now connected with the Fox-Case Movietone.

This invention relates to a new and improved electrical apparatus, particularly adapted for translating sound waves into light waves or variations of light waves which can be efficiently photographed or reproduced upon a film, thereby constituting a translatable film record of sound waves, particularly articulate or musical sound waves.

The invention includes as a separable element, an instantaneous varying light source of a most efficient character, highly actinic for photographic purposes and operable with comparatively low voltage, and peculiarly adapted for the production of a clear, distinct and readily translatable phonograph of electrical variations, especially as effected by variations in sound waves.

The apparatus as shown in Fig. 15, comprises a microphone -1- connected in circuit with a source of potential, as battery -2- and the primary -3- of a transformer -4-, in secondary -5- of which is connected in circuit with the filament -6- and grid -7- of an electron-discharge device -8-, the plate -9- of which is connected in circuit with a source of potential, as battery -10-, the primary -11- of a transformer -12- and the filament -6- of the electron-discharge device.

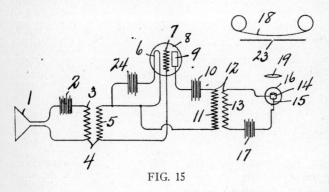

FIG. 15

The filament -6- may be heated in any suitable manner, as by connection in circuit with the source of potential, as battery -24-. The secondary -13- of the transformer -12- is preferably connected in circuit with a source of potential, as battery -17- and the two spaced electrodes -14- and -15- disposed within the bulb -16- which may, perhaps, preferably be formed of glass with a quartz end through which the rays pass to the photographing apparatus.

The electrodes may be of any desired form and as here illustrated, the electrode -14- is in the form of a comparatively small cylinder which may perhaps preferably be formed of a material such as aluminum to reduce the cathode sputtering and consequent darkening of the glass or quartz endpiece of the bulb -16-.

Preferably the electrodes are arranged in close proximity, as for instance, a distance of about 1/16th to ⅛th of an inch, altho wide variation may be had in that respect.

The essential feature of this invention resides particularly in the means provided for effecting operation of this bulb with comparatively low voltage, and further in the production of a variable light highly actinic for photographic purposes, and this is effected in accordance with the invention here disclosed by coating one or both of the electrodes with a rare earth oxide, such as thorium, cerium, etc., which materials in the combination here disclosed accomplish the object of this invention.

Josef Engl of Berlin, in July 1924 filed an application covering the "production of sound record photographic positive."

The invention relates to the prodution of sound record photographic positives. More particularly it relates to a process whereby a photographic negative may be made by acoustically-varied light, and a positive print made from such negative bearing a photographic record of varying intensities which may be utilized in the subsequent reproduction of sound therefrom. An object of the invention is the production of a process involving the making of the negative and therefrom the positive photographic record, in such a manner that certain inaccuracies of the photographic steps may be obviated; and that thereby, when sound is reproduced by the utilization of the positive, it will correspond quite accurately to the acoustically-varied light used for producing the negative, without distortions which might arise because of inaccuracies of the photographic process.

It should be understood that the photographic process comprising this invention may comprise part of a complete process or system for recording and subsequently reproducing sound, in which sound vibrations to be reproduced are directed to a form of microphone whereby an electrical current is produced which varies in correspondence with the sound vibrations which produced the same. This current flows in a circuit which includes a recording lamp, the light of which falls upon a suitable sensitized surface, such as a film strip which is moved across the beam of light. This recording light is maintained at constant luminosity when no sound waves are affecting the microphone, and its intensity varies above and below this constant, or average, luminosity when sound vibrations act upon the microphone. Accordingly, when the negative is thus made on the film and developed and a positive print made therefrom, the sound record should appear on the latter in the form of lines of varying density. When the sound is subsequently to be reproduced, the positive film is fed past a constant source of light which passes through the film to greater or less extent in accordance with the varying densities of the sound record lines or images thereon, the light thus passing through the film falling upon a light-sensitive device, such as a photo-electric cell. Electrical currents, which vary in correspondence with the light falling upon the photo-electric cell, will thereby be set up and these electrical currents may be led to some form of loud speaker, or sound reproducing device, whereby sound vibrations may be generated, and these should of course correspond as closely as possible to the original sound vibrations which were received by the microphone in the recording process.

In carrying out such a process, however, problems have arisen in the employment of the properties of the sensitive film as to the reactions of the latter to varying light intensities, in such manner that there shall be no inaccuracies in the photographic recording steps. The varying intensity of the light by which the negatives are made may be made to correspond quite closely to the original sound vibrations, and the final reproduction of sound may be made to correspond quite closely to the variations of current produced by the variations of light passing through the positive film and falling upon the photo-electric cell; but the perfections of process by which these results are attained will be to a considerable extent nullified if substantial inaccuracies are allowed to enter the complete system because of the inaccuracies which appear in the photographic steps as the same are commonly practiced.

In the problem, the solution of which is herein attained, there are two factors which must be considered. First, there should be an approximately constant proportion between the intensity of luminosity of the recording light by which the negative is made and the intensity of the light which passes through the positive film and falls upon the photocell in the sound reproduction process. The second factor to be considered is the desirability of having as great a part as possible of the positive film, or record, comparatively transparent, or as little light-absorptive as possible, because the loudness of the reproduction of sound by the loud speaker will vary in accordance with the amount of light which passes through the positive film, and acts upon the photo-cell. This can be accomplished when the transparency of the positive record-bearing film, or conversely, its light-absorptive power, has a possible range between zero and 100 per cent. This will be so when portions of the postive film corresponding to average intensity of the recording light have such a density that they will absorb 50 per cent of the light falling upon the same in the subsequent sound-reproducing operation. The average intensity of the recording light, referred to, is that intensity which corresponds to a total absence of sound to be recorded. The intensity of the recording light varies, above and below this average value, equally, when sound is being recorded. Accordingly, if the portions of the positive film corresponding to zero sound vibrations absorb 50 per cent of the incident light, the variations in density or light-absorptive power of the print, corresponding to the sound vibrations recorded, can extend equally in both directions, and vary from approximately zero to approximately 100 per cent. With this arrangement the entire range of sounds may be recorded, and also a great part of the film will be of large transparency.

Considering the light which is to act upon the photocell, in sound reproduction, as passing through a film of transparent material, celluloid or the like, bearing photographic images of varying darkness, the celluloid or other base is considered as entirely transparent and the light-absorptive properties of the film are considered as depending entirely upon the varying density of the photographic sound record thereon. If this condition is realized, namely that the absorption of the positive film shall be approximately fifty per cent of the light falling thereon when zero sound is to be reproduced, it follows that the light passing through the positive film upon the photo-cell, during reproduction, may vary throughout the entire range of intensity of acoustically varied recording lamp by which the negatives were made.

These conditions can only be fulfilled by special steps in the photographic process; this because of the fact that the variations of density in the negative, and the positive, are not strictly proportional, with normal development, to variations in the intensity of the recording light. This is particularly so where the illuminating intensity is small, corresponding to a large degree of transparency of the positive. In accordance with this invention these desired conditions are fulfilled by developing the negative in a special way, and making the positive print in a special way. (1,512,681)

In 1923 Lee DeForest came along with his "Phonofilm." This talking movie system was installed in a number of theatres, but for some reason did not find public favor. Perhaps this was due to the type of picture presented. Warner Bros., in conjunction with the Western Electric Company, introduced the "Vitaphone" in 1926. This system has met with great success, both as to subject produced and in the number of installations made. Fox-Case Movietone was installed in theatres in 1927, after years of research work by Theo. W. Case of Auburn and the Fox-Case Corp. This system has also met with great success.

TRANSMISSION OF SOUND

WHENEVER one investigates the source of a sound, he always finds that it can be traced to the motion of some material body. Thus, if he examine a violin string which is giving forth a note, he finds that it looks broader than when at rest, and that it has a hazy outline. He infers, therefore, that it is in rapid vibration. If he investigates a sounding tuning fork, he finds that if one prong is touched to the surface of a dish of mercury, it sends forth a series of ripples; if it is provided with a stylus and stroked across a smoked-glass plate, it produces a wavy line; if a light, suspended ball is brought into contact with it, the latter is thrown off with a considerable violence. He infers, therefore, that a sounding tuning fork is in rapid vibration. If he looks about for the source of any sudden noise, he finds that some object has fallen, or some explosion has taken place; in a word, that some violent motion of matter has been set up in some way. From these familiar facts we conclude that sound arises from the motions of matter.

Air is ordinarily the medium through which sound comes from its source to the ear of the observer. It is easy to show, however, that substances other than air may also serve to convey it.

Thus, if an ear is placed against one end of a long beam or table, a light scratching at the other end may be heard much more distinctly than if the ear is removed from the wood. Again, most boys are familiar with the fact that the clapping together of two stones may be heard even better when the ear and the stones are under water than when the experiment takes place in the air.

These experiments show that a gas like air is certainly no more effective in the transmission of sound than a liquid like water or a solid like wood.

Next, let us see whether or not matter is necessary at all for the transmission of sound.

Let an electric bell be suspended inside the receiver of an air pump by means of two fine springs which pass through a rubber stopper. Let the air be exhausted from the receiver by means of a good air pump. The sound of the bell will be found to become less and less pronounced. Let the air be suddenly readmitted. The volume of sound will at once increase.

Since, then, the nearer we approach a vacuum, the less distinct becomes the sound, we infer that sound cannot be transferred through a vacuum and that therefore the transmission of sound is effected through the agency of ordinary matter. In this respect sound differs from heat and light, which evidently pass with perfect readiness through a vacuum, since they reach the earth from the sun and stars.

In rooms of ordinary dimensions we are not conscious that it requires any time for sound to travel from its source to our ears. That it does, however, have a speed of propagation which is not too fast for easy detection is proved by the fact of common observation that a thunderclap follows usually at a considerable interval after the lightning flash, and that this interval is greater, the greater the distance of the observer from the flash; or again, that steam may be seen issuing from the whistle of a distant locomotive or steamboat some seconds before the sound is heard; or again that, in this latter case, the sound is heard for a corresponding interval after the steam has ceased to rise.

The speed of sound in air is found to increase with an increase in temperature. The amount of this increase is about 60 cm. per degree Centigrade. Hence the speed at 20° C. is about 343.2 m. per second. The above figures are equivalent to 1087 ft. per second at 0° C., or 1126 ft. per second at 20° C.

When a firecracker or toy cap explodes the powder is suddenly changed to a gas, the volume of which is enormously greater than the volume of the powder. The air is therefore suddenly pushed back in all directions from the centre of the explosion. This means that the air particles which lie about this centre are given violent outward velocities. When these outwardly impelled air particles collide with other particles, they give up their outward motion to these second particles, and these in turn pass it on to others, etc. It is clear, therefore, that the motion started by the explosion must travel on from particle to particle to an indefinite distance from the centre of the explosion. Furthermore, it is also clear that, although the motion travels on to great distances, the individual particles do not move far from their original positions; for it is easy to show experimentally that whenever an elastic body in motion collides with another similar body at rest, the colliding body simply transfers its motion to the body at rest, and comes itself to rest.

The loudness or intensity of the sound perceived by an observer depends simply upon the energy of the impulse which is communicated by the tympanum of the ear; and this in turn depends, first, upon the energy of the initial disturbance, and second, upon the distance of the ear from it. If, for example, the source of the sound is some particular vibrating rod or string, then the loudness observed at a given distance will depend simply upon the amplitude of vibration of the source, since the energy of the initial disturbance depends simply upon this amplitude.

The reason that a given sound grows weaker and weaker as we recede from its source is found in the fact that the original energy which was put into the disturbance gets distributed over more and more particles the farther the pulse recedes from the origin. Thus, if a sound is free to spread out in all directions

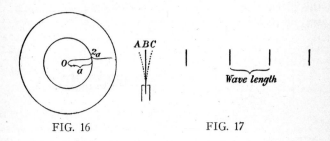

FIG. 16   FIG. 17

from a source O, Fig. 16, when it has reached a distance $2\,a$ from O, the original energy will be distributed over the surface of a sphere of radius $2\,a$, i.e., over four times as large a surface, and therefore over four times as many particles as when the pulse was at a distance a. Hence the intensity, or loudness at $2\,a$, can be but one-fourth as much as it was at a. We see, therefore, that under these ideal conditions the intensity of a sound pulse varies inversely as the square of the distance from the source.

The law of the last paragraph is only true when the sound is free to spread equally in all directions. If it is confined within a tube, so that the energy is continually communicated from one layer to another of equal area, instead of from one layer to another of larger area, it can be carried to great distances with no loss in intensity except that due to friction against the walls of the tube. This explains the efficiency of speaking tubes and megaphones.

In the preceding paragraphs we have confined attention to a single pulse traveling out from a centre of explosion. Let us next consider the sort of disturbance which is set up in the air by a continuously vibrating body like the prong of Fig. 17. Each time that this prong moves to the right it sends out a pulse which travels through the air at the rate of 1,100 ft. per sec-

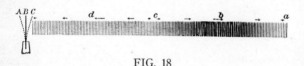

FIG. 18

ond, in exactly the manner described in the preceding paragraphs. Hence, if the reed is vibrating uniformly, we shall have a continuous succession of pulses following each other through the air at exactly equal intervals. Suppose, for example, that the prong makes 110 complete vibrations per second. Then at the end of one second the first pulse sent out will have reached a distance of 1,100 ft. Between this point and the prong there will be 110 pulses distributed at equal intervals, i.e., each two adjacent pulses will be just 10 ft. apart. If the prong made 220 vibrations per second, the distance between adjacent pulses would be 5 ft., etc. The distance between two adjacent pulses in such a train of waves is called a wave length.

If n represents the number of vibrations per second of a source of sound, l the wave length, and v the velocity with which the sound travels through the medium, it is evident from the example of the preceding paragraph that the following relation exits between these three quantities:

$$l = v/n, \text{ or } v = nl;$$

i.e., wave length is equal to velocity divided by the number of vibrations per second, or velocity is equal to number of vibrations per second times wave length.

Thus far, for the sake of simplicity, we have considered a train of waves as a series of thin, detached pulses separated by equal intervals of air at rest. In point of fact, however, the air in front of the prong B, Fig. 17, is being pushed forward not at one particular instant only, but during all the time that the prong is moving from A to C, i.e., through the time of one half vibration of the fork; and during all this time this forward motion is being transmitted to layers of air which are farther and farther away from the prong, so that when the latter reaches C all the air between B and some point c, Fig. 18, one-half wave length away is crowding forward, and is therefore in a state of compression or condensation. Again, as the prong moves back from C to A, since it tends to leave a vacuum behind it, the adjacent layer of air rushes in to fill up this space, the layer next adjoining follows, etc., etc., so that when the prong reaches A all the air between B and c, Fig. 18, is moving backward and is therefore in a state of diminished density or rarefaction. During all this time the preceding forward motion has advanced one-half wave length to the right, so that it now occupies the region between c and a, Fig. 18. Hence at the end of one complete vibration of the prong we may divide the air between it and a point one wave length away into two portions, one a region of condensation ac, and the other a region of rarefaction cB. The arrows in Fig. 18 represent the direction and relative magnitudes of the motions of the air particles in various portions of a complete wave.

At the end of n vibrations the first disturbance will have reached a distance n wave lengths from the fork, and each wave between this point and the fork will consist of a condensation and a rarefaction, so that sound waves may be said to consist of a series of condensations and rarefactions following one another through the air in the manner shown in Fig. 19.

abcdefghij

FIG. 19

Wave length may now be more accurately defined as the distance between two successive points of maximum condensation (b and f, Fig. 19) or of maximum rarefaction (d and h).

Condensations and rarefactions of sound waves are exactly analogous to the familiar crests and troughs of water waves. Thus, if Fig. 20 represents a series of ripples passing over the surface of water, the wave length of such a series is defined as the distance bf

between two crests, or the distance *dh,* or *ae,* or *cg,* or *mn,* between any two points which are in the same condition or phase of disturbance. The crests, i.e., the shaded portions, which are above the natural level of the water, correspond exactly to the condensations of sound waves, i.e., to the portions of air which are above the natural density. The troughs, i.e., the dotted portions, correspond to the rarefactions of sound waves, i.e., to the portions of air which are below in the natural density.

In spite of the analogy mentioned in the last paragraph, water waves differ from sound waves in one very important respect. In the former the particles of

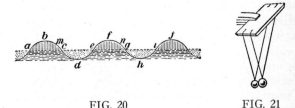

FIG. 20   FIG. 21

water are moving up and down while the wave is traveling along the surface, i.e., horizontally. Hence the motion of the particles is at right angles to the direction in which the wave is traveling. Such a wave is said to be a transverse wave, because the motion of the particles is transverse to the direction of propagation. In sound waves, however, the particles move back and forth in the line of propagation of the wave. Such waves are called longitudinal waves. Sound waves are always transmitted through any medium as longitudinal waves.

Reflection and Re-enforcement of Sound. That a sound wave in hitting a wall suffers reflection is shown by the familiar phenomenon of echo. A sharp sound made, for example, a quarter of a mile in front of a cliff or isolated large building, will be distinctly returned after a lapse of about two and a half seconds.

If the sound is made between two parallel cliffs, the echo may be repeated many times, because of successive reflections. It is then called a multiple echo. The roll of thunder is due to successive reflections of the original sound from clouds and other surfaces which are at different distances from the observer.

In ordinary rooms the walls are so close that the reflected waves return before the effect of the original sound on the ear has died out. Consequently the echo blends with and strengthens the original sound instead of interfering with it. This is why, in general, a speaker may be heard so much better indoors than in the open air. Since the ear cannot appreciate successive sounds as distinct if they come at intervals shorter than a tenth of a second, it will be seen from the fact that sound travels about 113 ft. in a tenth of a second that a wall which is closer than about 50 ft. cannot possibly produce a perceptible echo. In rooms which are large enough to give rise to troublesome echoes it is customary to hang draperies of some sort, so as to break up the sound waves and prevent regular reflection.

The conditions under which a reflection of sound must take place may readily be seen from the following experiment.

Let a small steel ball be suspended beside a large one, as in Fig. 21. Let the first ball be lifted up its arc and allowed to fall against the second. After the blow the first ball, instead of coming to rest, will be found to rebound from the larger ball with considerable velocity. The larger ball, on the other hand, will move but a comparatively short distance up its arc. Now let the larger ball be raised and allowed to fall against the smaller one. Upon collision the larger ball will not now be brought to rest, nor will it rebound, but it will move on in the direction in which it was originally going.

We conclude, therefore, that although an elastic particle which collides with an exactly similar particle transfers to the latter all of its energy, an elastic particle which collides with a heavier or lighter particle transfers only a part of its energy in the collision. In precisely the same way, when a sound pulse travels through a medium like air, each layer of which is exactly like that preceding, the whole of the energy is passed on from layer to layer, and no reflection is possible. But as soon as the wave strikes a medium of different density from that in which it has been traveling, only a part of the energy goes on into the new medium, and the remainder is propagated backward through the first meduim in the form of a reflected wave in precisely the same way in which the original pulse was propagated forward. The reflection of sound will then always take place whenever the molecular motion which constitutes a sound wave reaches a medium of different density from that in which it has been traveling. It is on account of differences in the homogeneity of the atmosphere on different days that sound "carries" so much better at some times than at others. Lack of homogeneity results in a dissipation of the energy of the sound waves by repeated reflections from layers of different density.

If the new medium is denser than the old, as when a sound wave traveling in air approaches a wooden wall, the forward-moving particles of an on-coming condensation rebound when they strike the wall, precisely as did the smaller of the two balls in the preceding experiment. This rebound is propagated back through the old medium as a motion in the same direction as that of propagation of the reflected wave, i.e., as a condensation. But if the new medium is rarer than the old, as when sound passes from water into air, when the particles of an oncoming condensation strike the particles of the lighter medium they overshoot their positions of rest, precisely as did the heavier ball in the second experiment with the unequal balls, and thus create a rarefaction behind them in the first medium. We learn, therefore, that a condensation is reflected from a denser medium as a condensation, from a rarer medium as a rarefaction. A similar analysis shows that a rarefaction is reflected from a denser medium as a rarefaction, from a rare medium as a condensation.

Let a watch be hung at the focus of a large concave mirror. On account of the reflection from the surface of the mirror a fairly well-defined beam of sound will be thrown out in front of the mirror, so that, if both watch and mirror are hung on a single support and the whole turned in different directions toward a number of observers, the ticking will be distinctly heard by those directly in front of the mirror, but not by those at one side. If a second mirror is held in the path of this beam, as in Fig. 22, the sound may be again brought to a focus, so that if the ear is placed in the focus of this second mirror, or better still, if a small funnel which is connected with the ear by a rubber tube is held in this focus, the ticking of the watch may sometimes be heard hundreds of feet away.

Resonance is the re-enforcement or intensification

of sound because of the union of direct and reflected waves.

Thus, let one prong of a vibrating tuning fork, which makes, for example, 512 vibrations per second, be held over the mouth of a tube an inch or so in diameter, arranged as in Fig. 24, so that as the vessel *A* is raised or lowered the height of the water in the tube may be adjusted at will. It will be found that, as the position of the water is slowly lowered from the top of the tube, a very marked re-enforcement of the sound will occur at a certain point.

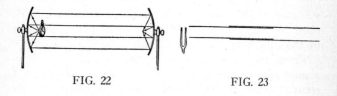

FIG. 22   FIG. 23

Let other forks of different pitch be tried in the same way. It will be found that the lower the pitch of the fork the lower must be the water in the tube in order to get the best re-enforcement. This means that the longer the wave length of the note which the fork produces the longer must be the air column in order to obtain resonance.

We conclude, therefore, that a fixed relation exists between the wave length of a note and the length of the air column which will re-enforce it.

If we calculate the wave length of the note of the fork by dividing the speed of sound by the vibration rate of the fork, we shall find that, in every case, the length of air column which gives the best response is approximately one fourth wave length. The reason for this is evident when we consider that the length must be such as to enable the reflected wave to return to the mouth just in time to unite with the direct wave which is at that instant being sent off by the prong. Thus, when the prong is first starting down from the position *A*, see Fig. 25, it starts the beginning of a condensation down the tube. If this motion is to return to the mouth just in time to unite with the direct wave sent off by the prong, it must get back at the instant that the prong is first starting up from the position *C*. In other words, the pulse must go down the tube and back again while the prong is making a half vibration. This means that the path down and back must be a half wave length, and hence that the length of the tube must be a fourth wave length.

From the above analysis it will appear that there should also be resonance if the reflected wave does not return to the mouth till the fork is starting back its second time from *C*, i.e., at the end of one and a half vibrations instead of a half vibration. The distance from the fork to the water and back would then be one and a half wave lengths; i.e., the water surface would be a half wave length farther down the tube than at first. The tube length would therefore now be three fourths of a wave length.

Let the experiment be tried. A similar response will indeed be found, as predicted, a half wave length farther down the tube. This response will be somewhat weaker than before, as the wave has lost some of its energy in traveling a longer distance through the tube. It may be shown in a similar way that there will be resonance where the tube length is $\frac{5}{4}$, $\frac{7}{4}$, or indeed any old number of quarter wave lengths.

If the bottom of the tube Figs. 24 or 25 had been closed by a medium lighter than air, then a downward-moving condensation would have been reflected as an upward-moving rarefaction, i.e., as an upward-moving wave in which the motion of the particles would have been down instead of up. Hence, if this upward-moving wave is to get back to the mouth of the tube

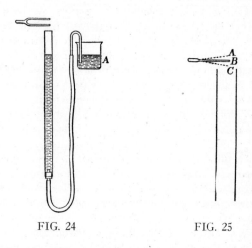

FIG. 24   FIG. 25

just in time to unite with and therefore re-enforce a direct wave sent off by the prong, it must return, not now at the instant that the prong is starting up from C, but rather at the instant at which it is starting down again from A, i.e., after an interval corresponding to one complete vibration of the prong. Hence the length of the air chamber will need to be, in this case, a half wave length instead of a quarter wave length, if resonance is to be obtained.

Now, as a matter of fact, a pulse traversing a simple tube which is open at the lower end experiences at this end a reflection of precisely the same kind which it would experience if it struck a rarer medium, for within the tube the pulse has been free to push forward only in one direction, but as it reaches the open end it suddenly becomes free to expand in all directions; i.e., it encounters at this point less resistance to its forward motion than it has encountered within the tube, and therefore it acts precisely as it would in going from a denser to a rarer medium. The correctness of this assertion is proved by the following experiment.

Let the tuning fork be held in front of an open pipe (8 or 10 in. long) the length of which is made adjustable by slipping back and forth over it a tightly fitting roll of writing paper, Fig. 23. It will be found that for one particular length this open pipe will respond quite as loudly as did the closed pipe, but the responding length will be found to be just twice as great as before.

We learn, then, that the shortest resonant length of an open pipe is one half wave length. It is evident that there must also be resonance when the pipe length is one wave length, for then the first reflected wave will get back just in time to unite with the third forward motion of the prong. Similarly, there will be resonance when the pipe length is $\frac{3}{2}$, $\frac{4}{2}$, $\frac{5}{2}$, or any number, odd or even, of half wave lengths.

If the vibrating fork at the mouth of the tubes in the preceding experiments is replaced by a train of waves coming from a distant source, precisely the same analysis leads to the conclusion that the waves reflected from the bottom of the tube will re-enforce the oncoming waves when the length of the tube is any odd number of quarter wave lengths in the case of a closed pipe, or any number of half wave lengths in the case of an open pipe. It is clear, therefore, that every air chamber will act as a resonator for trains of waves of a certain wave length. This is why a conch shell held to the ear is always heard to hum with a particular note. Feeble waves which produce no impression upon the unaided ear gain sufficient strength when re-enforced by the shell to become audible. When the air chamber is of irregular form it is not usually possible to calculate to just what wave length it will respond, but it is always easy to determine experimentally what particular wave length it is capable of re-enforcing. The resonators on which tuning forks are mounted are air chambers which are of just the right dimensions to respond to the note given out by the fork.

Let a tuning fork be struck and held in the hand. The sound will be entirely inaudible except to those quite near. Let the base of the sounding fork be pressed firmly against the table. The sound will be found to be enormously intensified. Let another fork be held against the same table. Its sound will also be re-enforced. In this case, then, the table intensifies the sound of any fork which is placed against it, while an air column of a certain size could intensify only a single note.

The cause of the response in the two cases is wholly different. In the last case the vibrations of the fork are transmitted through its base to the table top and force the latter to vibrate in its own period. The vibrating table top, on account of its large surface, sets a comparatively large mass of air into motion and therefore sends a wave of great intensity to the ear; while the fork alone, with its narrow prongs, was not able to impart much energy to the air. Vibrations like those of the table top are called forced vibrations because they can be produced with any fork, no matter what its period. Sounding-boards in pianos and other stringed instruments act precisely as does the table in this experiment; i.e., they are set into forced vibrations by any note of the instrument, and re-enforce it accordingly.

Since two sound waves are able to unite so as to re-enforce each other, it ought also to be possible to make them unite so as to interfere with or destroy each other. In other words, under the proper conditions the union of two sounds ought to produce silence.

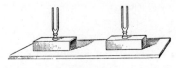

FIG. 26

Let two mounted tuning forks of the same pitch be set side by side, as in Fig. 26. Let the two forks be struck in quick succession with a soft mallet, for example, a rubber stopper on the end of a rod. The two notes will blend and produce a smooth, even tone. Then let a piece of wax or a small coin be stuck to a prong of one of the forks. This diminishes slightly the number of vibrations which this fork makes per second, since it increases its mass. Again let the two forks be sounded together. The former smooth tone will be replaced by a throbbing or pulsating one. This is due to the alternate destruction and re-enforcement of the sounds produced by the two forks. The phenomenon is called the phenomenon of beats.

The mechanism of the alternate destruction and re-enforcement may be understood from the following. Suppose that one fork makes 256 vibrations per second (see the dotted line AC in Fig. 27.), while the other makes 255 (see the heavy line AC in Fig. 27). If, at the beginning of a given second the two forks are swinging together so that they simultaneously send out condensations to the observer, these condensations will of course unite so as to produce a double effect upon the ear (see A', Fig. 27). Since now one fork gains one complete vibration per second over the other, at the end of the second considered the two forks will again be vibrating together, i.e., sending out condensations which add their effects as before (see C'). In the middle of

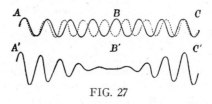

FIG. 27

this second, however, the two forks are vibrating in opposite directions (see B); i.e., one is sending out rarefactions while the other sends out condensations. At the ear of the observer the union of the rarefaction (backward motion of the air particles) produced by one fork with the condensation (forward motion) produced by the other, results in no motion at all, provided the two motions have the same energy; i.e., in the middle of the second the two sounds have united to produce silence (see B'). If the two sounds are of unequal intensity; the destruction will not be complete, the minimum representing the difference between the two intensities, and the maximum the sum.

It will be seen from the above that the number of beats per second must be equal to the difference in the vibration numbers of the two forks. To test this conclusion, let more wax or a heavier coin be added to the weighted prong; the number of beats per second will be increased. Diminishing the weight will reduce the number of beats per second.

The experiment, therefore, shows an easy and accurate method of determining the difference in vibration rates of two sounding bodies which have nearly but not quite the same pitch. It is only necessary to sound them together and to note the number of beats per second. This number is the difference in their vibration numbers. If weighting either body increases the number of beats, that body was the slower; if weighting this body diminishes the number of beats, that body was the faster.

The voice is produced by forcing air from the lungs through the opening between a pair of stretched membranes, each of which is able to cover half of the larynx or passage from the lungs to the mouth. These membranes are called the Vocal Chords, and when not in use for speaking or singing, their free edges are widely separated, so as not to interfere with the breathing.

By means of muscles these membranes can be stretched and their edges brought together. If air is now forced between them, their edges are set in vibration, and the air issues in a series of puffs, which give rise to a musical note.

The pitch of the note is varied mainly by altering the tension of the chords, the changes of tension being brought about by muscles attached to the larynx. The pitch and quality of the note can probably also be altered by changes in the distribution of the mass of the chords. On their under surface there is a layer of membrane, which can be moved toward or from the edge, thus weighting the vibrating part to a greater or less extent, and so altering the period and nature of the vibrations. The adjacent edges of the chords probably touch each other in the course of each vibration, and so make the stream of air discontinuous. The result of this discontinuity is that Fourier's analysis gives a long series of harmonics in the note produced. It is possible to detect as many as 15 or 16 in the note sung by a powerful bass voice.

The sound has to pass through the mouth on its way to the outer air, and the mouth and its adjoining cavities have natural periods of their own. Consequently such harmonics as approximate in pitch to any of the natural periods of the mouth will be strengthened by resonance, and the quality of the note will be altered. The pitch of the mouth regarded as a resonator can be altered at will, either by altering its volume, or by altering the size of its opening. Changes of volume can be brought about either by moving the tongue, or by opening the jaws more or less widely, and changes of opening by means of the lips. It will be seen therefore that we can make changes in the quality of the voice by altering the shape and size of the mouth, and it is by such changes that the different vowels are produced.

A musical note is heard only when the number of vibrations per second is between certain limits, which are different for different persons.

If the vibrations are slower than about 30 per second they do not blend into a note, but are heard separately.

Even when they are somewhat about 30 per second, they do not give the sensation of a note, unless they are of the kind known as Simple Harmonic Vibrations.

When the vibrations are very rapid, they cease to produce any impression on the ear. The sensitiveness of the ear to high notes falls off with advancing age. Children can generally hear notes with 20,000 vibrations per second, elderly people cannot generally hear anything above 15,000.

We conclude then that within these limits the pitch of a note depends on the number of vibrations executed per second by the body which gives out the sound. This number is called the Frequency of the vibrations.

THE PHONOGRAPH

THE Phonograph was invented by Edison in 1877. It has been little altered from its original form, the general principle of the instrument remaining the same.

Fig. 28 shows the essential parts in a diagrammatic form. A is a conical mouthpiece by which the sounds to be reproduced are concentrated on a diaphragm B.

The diaphragm, which may be made of glass, metal, mica, or other material, has a sharp needle fixed to the centre of its lower surface, the pointed end of the needle pressing against a rotating cylinder of hard wax. The cylinder is rotated at a uniform rate by clockwork or other means, and is mounted on an axis on which a screw is cut, so that it moves along its axis as it rotates. By this means the trace made on the wax by the needle is in the form of a helix from end to end of the cylinder.

In some forms of the phonograph the trace is made on a disc which revolves round its centre, and the recording point is moved gradually outwards from the centre as the plate rotates, so as to cut a spiral curve in the wax.

The air-waves that enter the cone set the diaphragm in vibration, and the needle cuts a furrow in the wax, the depth of the furrow varying from point to point in accordance with the varying displacement of the diaphragm.

When the cutting of the furrow has been completed, the cone and diaphragm are raised, and the cylinder returned to its starting point. The cone is then lowered again into its place, and the cylinder set in rotation.

The needle rises and falls as the depth of the groove varies, and makes the diaphragm repeat the vibrations it performed when the groove was being cut. The diaphragm communicates its vibrations to the air, and thus the features of the original sound are reproduced. In practice the cutting needle is not used for reproducing the sound. It is so sharp that it will not rise and fall in the furrow, and soon destroys the trace. A needle with a rounded point is therefore used to replace the cutting needle when the sound is to be reproduced.

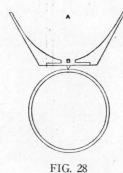

FIG. 28

The instrument copies the features of the original sound very closely. The voice of the speaker can be recognized, and the qualities of the notes of different musical instruments are easily distinguished. It fails to some extent when a sound is characterized by the presence of high harmonics, for the diaphragm cannot vibrate rapidly enough to record them on the cylinder.

If speech is to be reproduced at the same pitch as the original, the cylinder or disc must rotate at the same rate when the record is made, and when the speech is reproduced. If the cylinder is rotated more rapidly during reproduction, the pitch is raised. Not only does the pitch of the fundamental rise, but also the pitch of all the harmonics, and therefore the harmonic relations of the constituents is preserved, and the quality of the note is unchanged.

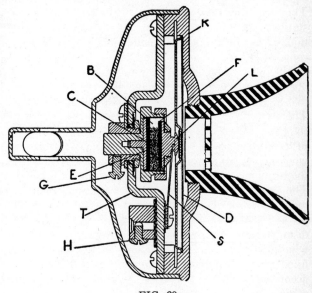

FIG. 29

TELEGRAPHY AND TELEPHONY

An ordinary wire telegraph system consists simply of an electric circuit connecting two stations and simple equipment inserted directly in the line at each station. The same kind of equipment is generally used at each station, and communication can be had in either direction. On short lines the equipment of each station consists of a "key" and a "sounder" connected in series in the line. The key is a simple device for rapidly opening and closing the circuit and is so constructed that it can be conveniently and rapidly operated by hand. There is only a small clearance between the contacts of the key. When the key is not being operated and is up in its normal position the circuit is open. At all times when no signals are being transmitted at a given station the terminals of the key are short-circuited by a switch. The sounder is an electromagnet with an armature so mounted, close to the poles of the electromagnet on a pivoted arm, that the armature moves through a small distance when the current passes through the magnet windings. The end of the arm moves between two fixed tops, which may be screws. The arm moves in accordance with the current impulses on the line, corresponding to the opening and closing of the key at the distant station, and the contact of the end of the arm with the stops causes a click both when contact is made with the lower and with the upper stop. Signals are transmitted by means of depressing the key to make "dots" and "dashes." A dot is made by depressing the key for an instant; a dash is made by holding the key down a little longer. A dash is equal in length to three dots. Messages are transmitted by a "code" or arrangement of groups of dots and dashes representing the letters of the alphabet. The code used on land lines in the United States is the "Morse" code. On the Continent of Europe land lines use the "Continental" code or "International Morse code." This code is used throughout the world in radio telegraphy.

In ordinary practice there is only one wire between two stations, and one terminal of the station apparatus at each end is connected to the earth, through which the return current flows. Ordinarily a number of intermediate stations are cut in on a telegraph line at points between the two terminal stations. Telegraph lines are usually operated as closed circuits—that is, current is flowing through the line at all times except when the line is actually in use for transmitting signals. The power for operation may be supplied by a closed-circuit battery, such as a battery of "gravity" cells, or by a direct-current generator. On all except short lines the line current is not strong enough to operate a sounder directly so that signals can be read, and a relay is connected in the line. The operation of the relay by the line current opens and closes a local circuit which operates the sounder.

The telegraph system here described represents the simplest case. In actual practice many modifications may be made. Signals may be transmitted and recorded at high speed by automatic apparatus. There are very few operators who can copy as many as 50 words per minute, but with automatic apparatus several hundred words per minute may be transmitted. With suitable apparatus it is possible at one time to transmit several messages over the same wire without one message interfering at all with the others; this is called "multiplex" telegraphy.

In ordinary telephony the voice itself is electrically transmitted over wires and reproduced at a distant point. The essential parts of a simple telephone system are (a) a device called the "transmitter," by means of which sound vibrations cause corresponding variations of an electric current, (b) a device for changing the electric current variations back into the corresponding sounds, (c) an electric circuit for connecting the two devices.

In the telephone exchanges in use in large cities the connecting circuit and switching apparatus are very intricate. In some cities automatic switching equipment is in use for connecting subscribers at the central office. This equipment operates automatically directly under the control of the calling subscriber, without an operator at the central office, and may be very elaborate.

The device by means of which sound vibrations cause corresponding variations of an electric current is usually the carbon microphone transmitter. This type of transmitter is a speech-controlled variable resistance, and its operation is based on the fact that the resistance of carbon varies with pressure changes. A low voltage, as from a battery of a few cells, is connected to opposite sides of a small cup containing carbon granules. The pressure on the carbon granules is controlled by the position of a metal diaphragm on which the sound is impressed.

Fig. 29 shows a telephone transmitter of a type which is in general use throughout the United States, called the "solid-back" transmitter. This name is used because the cup containing the carbon granules is supported on a solid back which consists of a metal bar attached at its ends to the case of the transmitter. In the figure D is the diaphragm, usually an aluminum disc about $2\frac{1}{2}$ inches in diameter. T is the solid back, on which is mounted the metal cup B, containing the carbon granules C. At the back of the cup is a small hardened carbon plate E, which serves as one electrode of the carbon microphone. At the front is another very hard carbon plate F, which serves as a lid for the small metal cup. The diameter of this plate is a little less than the diameter of the inside of the cup, but the cup is completely closed by a flexible mica disc, which is attached to the rim of the cup and to the carbon disc. This carbon lid or cover forms the second electrode of the transmitter. The button L attached to the carbon plate F is maintained in contact with the diaphragm by a metal spring S, which serves also to damp the vibrations of the diaphragm. The space between the carbon cover F and the back electrode E is nearly filled with carbon granules, and the electrodes E and F are so insulated that the electric current in the transmitter circuit, in passing from one electrode to the other, passes through the entire mass of carbon granules. The two wires leading to the transmitter are connected to the binding posts G and H. The metal face K of the transmitter is made heavy to prevent excessive vibration, and the exposed metal parts are usually insulated from the current-carrying parts. In practice it is not usually found desirable to have the transmitter extremely sensitive, because outside noises are then transmitted, and it is therefore difficult to understand the speech. The current through the usual type of microphone transmitter is about 0.2 ampere, and the power consumed in the transmitter is about 2 watts.

The microphone transmitters used in radiotelephony

at the present time do not differ essentially from those used in wire telephony, and, in fact, the identical transmitter usually furnished by operating telephone companies can be used for radiotelephony.

The device by means of which the variations in the electric current reproduce the corresponding sounds is the telephone receiver, which is made in a variety of forms. The type of receiver, shown in Fig. 30 called the "watchcase" receiver, is often used in wire telephony, and is almost universally used in both radiotele-

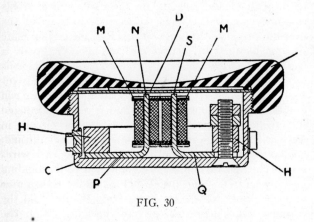

FIG. 30

graphy and radiotelephony. Two watchcase receivers are commonly used together, connected by a metallic "headband," constituting a "head set." In Fig. 30, C is a cup which is the case of the receiver. This cup may be metal or hard rubber or a composition. In the bottom of this cup a permanent magnet of horseshoe shape is placed; the ends of this permanent magnet are shown at HH. To the ends of the permanent magnet are attached the bent, soft-iron pole pieces NP, SQ. The earpiece E is usually hard rubber or a composition and is threaded to the cup C. Around each pole piece a coil of fine insulated wire is wound, forming the windings MM. These two windings are usually connected in series, so that the received current passes through both windings.

In some instruments for use with feeble currents the wire is very fine and the two coils contain some thousands of turns, sometimes as many as 10,000 turns. In the ordinary standard receiver the number of turns is, roughly, about 1,000. The resistance measured with direct current of a receiver for wire telephony may vary considerably, but for the standard receiver is usually about 100 ohms. A receiver designed for the very feeble currents sometimes used in radio communication may have a d. c. resistance of 8,000 ohms, and seldom has a resistance of less than 1,000 ohms. The coils of a receiver, particularly those designed for radio work, have considerable inductance, and at high frequencies the impedance in ohms of the coils of the receiver may be many times the resistance of the coils measured with direct current. The larger the number of turns used, the greater is the magnetic effect in the receiver for a current of given strength.

Above the pole pieces and very close to them is a thin, circular, soft-iron disk D, called the "diaphragm." The diaphragm of a receiver can be seen through the hole in the center of the earpiece. The distance between the pole pieces and the diaphragm is important in determining the sensitivity of the receiver; in standard instruments this distance is about 0.003 inch. The permanent magnet pulls the diaphragm toward the pole pieces a certain distance, which depends upon the flexibility of the diaphragm. The variations in the current in the receiver windings, corresponding to the sound vibrations of the voice spoken into the transmitter, produce corresponding variations in the magnetic field of the pole pieces, and the diaphragm moves in accordance with these variations and reproduces the voice spoken into the transmitter.

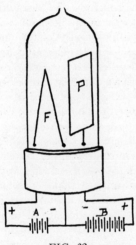

FIG. 32

F—Filament. P—Plate.
A—Battery for Heating Filament.
B—Battery for Sending Current Through Space
    Between Plate and Filament.

VACUUM TUBES

THE success of the talking picture is due in no small measure to the photo-electric cell and the vacuum tube, the photo-electric cell is used both in making the sound track on the motion picture film and again to convert the photographic sound record into light pulses in the showing of the picture. The vacuum tube is used to amplify the voice or music before it reaches the photo-electric cell when making the picture and sound record, it is also used to amplify the sound received through the photo-electric cell so that it may be heard in the horns or loud-speakers when projecting the picture.

There is nothing mysterious about the working principle of either the photo-electric cell or the vacuum tube and we believe that by following the text of this chapter carefully much of the seemingly mysterious workings of these tubes will be cleared away.

Vacuum tubes may be used for a variety of purposes —to generate, to amplify, and to modulate radio oscillations, as well as to detect them—they now are used in most types of radio apparatus. New applications have come rapidly, and there is every reason to believe that further developments may be expected. The electron tube is of primary importance in radio communication, but it has many important applications in other fields of electrical engineering, particularly in ordinary telephony with wires, where its use makes possible conversation between points separated by a distance of 3,000 miles. One fact of importance is that such tubes make possible the use of apparatus that is easily portable—a primary consideration in military communication, and

90

of importance also in various commercial applications. The principles which underlie the operation of electron tubes and their action under the widely different conditions met in actual practice therefore deserve careful study.

The name "electron tube" is derived from the fact that the action of the tube is due to very small particles of matter called "electrons." An electron is much smaller than an atom, and is the building block of which atoms are constructed. An idea of the extremely small size of the electron may be obtained from the estimate that in a very tiny spherical globule of copper having a diameter of one one-hundred-thousandth of an inch, there are about 20 billion electrons. The atom was formerly regarded as the smallest particle of matter which could exist; something like 25,000 hydrogen atoms would have to be placed in contact in a row to make up a length of one ten-thousandth of an inch. The weight of an electron is only about one two-thousandths of the weight of a hydrogen atom. An electron carries a charge of negative electricity whose value can be measured. Since the comparatively recent general recognition by scientific men of the existence of the electron, many ideas formerly held as the explanations of various physical phenomena have been considerably modified. The fact that the electron carries a charge of negative electricity makes possible the use of the electron tube in radio communication.

If two wires are connected to a battery, one to each terminal, the other two ends of the wires may be brought very close together in air, yet so long as they do not touch no current flows between them. The two ends may be inclosed in a bulb like that of an incandescent electric lamp and the air pumped out, and still so long as the ends are separated no current will flow. Thus, when the filament in an incandescent electric lamp breaks, the current stops and the light goes out.

About 1884 Edison discovered that if inside an exhausted incandescent electric lamp of the ordinary type, containing a filament whose two ends were connected to two wires insulated from each other, there was introduced a third insulated from the filament connections and maintained at a voltage positive with respect to the filament, then a current would flow across the vacuum inside the tube from the third wire to the filament as long as the filament was incandescent, but that the current ceased as soon as the filament became cold. This phenomenon is generally called the "Edison effect." It is due to the fact that the incandescent filament shoots off electrons at high velocity, each carrying its charge of negative electricity, and that the electrons are attracted to the positively charged third wire. The passage to the third wire of the negative charges of the electrons is equivalent to the flow of a current between the filament and third wire. In order that a current of one-billionth of an ampere should flow between the filament and the plate, it is necessary that more than six billion electrons should pass each second from the filament to the plate. It should be particularly noted that while the electrons move from the heated filament to the cold third wire, the current passes from the third wire to the filament, according to the usual idea that the direction of an electric current is from the positive (higher) to the negative (lower) voltage. This distinction between the direction of *electron flow* and the direction of *current flow* should be carefully noted.

As each electron leaves the filament, the filament acquires a charge of positive electricity equal in amount to the negative charge carried by the electron. If no voltage is applied to the third wire, electrons will still be emitted by the incandescent filament, but will travel only a very short distance before being attracted back to the filament by the positive charge acquired by the filament. The voltage applied to the third wire must be sufficient to overcome this attraction of the filament. No current will flow if the negative terminal of the battery is connected to the third wire, because the electrons will not be attracted by the negatively charged third wire, and, in fact, will be repelled back into the filament.

A tube containing a filament and one additional wire or other piece of metal, is called a two-electrode tube, the filament being considered as one electrode, and the additional piece of metal the second electrode.

The above explanation of the mechanism of the flow of current between the filament and plate in an electron tube applies to a tube having a very perfect vacuum. If there is more than the merest trace of gas remaining in the tube, the operation is more complicated, and a larger current will usually flow with the same applied voltage. This happens in the following manner.

In a rarefied gas some of the electrons present are constituent parts of atoms and some are free. These free electrons move about with great velocity, and if one of them strikes an atom it may dislodge another electron from the atom. Under the action of the emf. between plate and filament the newly freed electron will acquire velocity in one direction—the direction in which the colliding electron is moving—and the positively charged remainder of the atom, called an "ion," will move in the opposite direction. Thus both of the parts of the disrupted atom become carriers of electricity and contribute to the flow of current through the gas. This action of a colliding electron upon an atom is called "ionization by collision," and, on account of it, relatively large plate currents are obtained in electron tubes having a poor vacuum. The earlier tubes were of this sort, but at the present time most tubes are made with a better vacuum than formerly, so that ionization by collision is responsible for but a small part of the current flow.

At first it would seem to be an advantage to have ionization by collision, because a larger plate current can be obtained, but there are two difficulties which have proved so great that tubes are now usually so made as to have only the pure electron flow. The first of these difficulties is a rapid deterioration of the filament when there is flowing a large plate current which is caused by ionization by collision. The positively charged parts of the atoms are driven violently against the negatively charged filament, and since they are much more massive than electrons (an oxygen or nitrogen ion has about 25,000 times the mass of an electron), this bombardment actually seems to tear away the surface of the filament. A second disadvantage of tubes with poor vacuum is that too large a battery voltage may cause a "blue-glow" discharge.

Two similar tubes with poor vacuum seldom, if ever, contain just the same quantity of gas, and therefore their electrical characteristics may be considerably different. For this reason it is not ordinarily practicable to connect in parallel two tubes having poor vacuum. Tubes with high vacuum, on the other hand, can be constructed very uniformly, so that a number can be connected in parallel. It is often advantageous to be able to connect several tubes in parallel in generating sets.

Tubes containing a little gas, i.e., having a poor vacuum, are often called "gas tubes," or "soft tubes." Tubes with high vacuum are often called "hard tubes." "Soft" tubes are particularly useful as detectors, and if properly selected and used may be much more satisfactory as detectors than "hard" tubes of similar construction.

Let us consider what happens in a two-electrode tube having a good vacuum, when there is a variation in either the temperature of the filament or the voltage of the battery connected between the plate and filament.

Suppose first that the filament temperature is kept constant. Then a definite number of electrons will be sent out per second. The number of electrons that travel across the tube and reach the plate per second determines the magnitude of the current through the plate circuit. The number of electrons that reaches the plate increases with an increase of the battery connected between the plate and filament (Fig. 32). If this voltage is continuously increased, a value will be reached at which all the electrons sent out from the filament arrive at the plate. No further increase of current is possible by increasing the voltage, and this value of current is called the saturation current.

If now the temperature of the filament is raised to a higher constant value by means of the filament-heating battery and the same voltage steps again applied, the plate current curve will coincide with that obtained before, until the bend is reached; then it will rise higher. The explanation of this is that the number of electrons sent out by the filament increases with the temperature approximately as the square of the excess of the fila-

ment temperature above red heat, and thus more electrons are available to be drawn over to the plate. Thus
a higher value of plate current will be obtained before
reaching the limiting condition when all the electrons
emitted arrive at the plate. When this finally happens,
the curve, as before, bends over until nearly horizontal.

Suppose now that the voltage of the plate battery is
kept at a constant value and the filament temperature is
gradually raised by increasing the current from the
filament-heating battery. The number of electrons sent
out will continue to increase as the temperature rises.
The electric field intensity due to the presence of the
negative electrons in the space between filament and
plate may at last equal and neutralize that due to the
positive potential of the plate, so that there is no force
acting on the electrons near the filament. This effect
of the electrons in the space is called the "space charge
effect." It must not be supposed that the space charge
effect is caused by the same electrons all the time.
Electrons near the plate are constantly entering it, but
new electrons emitted by the filament are entering the
space, so that the total number between filament and
plate remains constant at a given temperature. After
the temperature of the filament has reached a point
where the effect of the electrons present in the space
between filament and plate neutralizes the effect of the
plate voltage, any further increase of the filament temperature is unable to cause an increase of the current.
The tendency of the filament to emit more electrons per
second, because of the increased temperature, is offset
by the increase in space charge effect which would result if electrons were emitted more rapidly, or, more
exactly, for any extra electrons emitted, an equal num-

ber of those in the space are repelled back into the filament.

Between the filament and plate of a tube we may insert another piece of metal. This third electrode interposed in the stream of electrons between filament and grid is usually in the form of a metallic gauze or a grid of fine wires, and is generally called the "grid." A tube which contains a filament, plate, and grid is called a three-electrode tube and is capable of many more uses than the two-electrode tube. The addition of the third electrode makes it possible to increase or decrease the current between plate and filament through wide limits. If a voltage is impressed upon the grid by means of a third battery connected between the filament and grid, the space charge effect will be modified. The electrons traveling from filament to plate pass between the wires forming the grid. If the grid is given a potential which is negative with respect to the filament the grid will repel the electrons, but many of them will still pass through, and reach the plate, because of their high velocity, because the positive plate potential still affects them to some extent. If the grid potential is made still more negative the plate current will diminish until finally it may be stopped entirely.

Suppose, however, that the grid is given a positive potential instead of negative. Electrons are now attracted to the grid as well as to the plate, and more electrons are now drawn toward the plate than would otherwise pass, so that the plate current increases. The charge of the grid partially neutralizes the effect of the space charge. As in the two-electrode tube, a limit to the magnitude of the plate current will finally be reached, when the space charge caused by the large

number of negative electrons in the tube fully counter-
acts the influence of the positive charges on grid and
plate. The attainment of the limiting or *saturation*
value of the plate current is assisted by the absorption
of more electrons into the grid if its positive potential
is increased. This absorption gives rise to a relatively
small current in the circuit *FGCF*, which is called the
grid current.

The Tube as an Amplifier. An electron tube acts as
a detector or rectifier because an alternating voltage
applied to the grid circuit can be made to produce un-
symmetrical oscillations in the plate circuit. While the
tube is thus acting as a detector it is also, as a matter
of fact, acting as an amplifier—that is, oscillations of
greater power are produced in the plate circuit for a
given alternating voltage in the grid circuit than would
be produced by the same voltage directly in the plate
circuit. This explains why the electron tube may be a
more sensitive detector than the crystal detector, which
acts as a rectifier only.

It is sometimes desired to amplify an alternating
current without any rectifying or detecting action.
This is done by keeping a voltage on the grid of such
value that the symmetry of the oscillations in the plate
circuit is not altered. Thus, if there is a steady voltage
applied on the grid of such value that the plate current
is on the part of the characteristic curve that is nearly
straight, then a small change in grid voltage in either
direction causes the plate current to increase or decrease the same amount. For instance, if the grid voltage is increased from v to w (Fig. 33) or decreased by
an equal amount from v to u, the current will, in the
first case, increase from a to c and in the second case

fall off by an equal amount, from a to b. In other words, the wave form of the grid voltage variation will be repeated in the fluctuating plate current. The latter will now be equivalent to an alternating current superimposed upon the steady plate current from the plate battery. The magnitude of the alternating-current part of the plate current will be greater, the steeper the slope of the curve at the point P.

For the same voltage acting in the two circuits the power expended in maintaining the oscillations of the grid current is far less than that involved in the corresponding variations in the plate current. The signals may be thought of as exerting a sort of relay action on the plate circuit, causing magnified power to be drawn from the plate battery. The tube is said in this case to act as an "amplifier." The variations of current in the grid circuit have been compared to the slide valve of an engine, since they admit energy from the battery into the plate circuit much as the slide valve admits energy into the cylinder of the engine. The oscillations impressed on the grid circuit may be of high radio frequency or of an audible frequency of perhaps 300 to 3,000 cycles per second.

To utilize the amplified alternating current in the plate circuit, the primary of a transformer T (Fig. 34) may be placed in the plate circuit. From the secondary of this transformer the alternating current is delivered to a detector, which may be an electron tube operating as a rectifier or a crystal detector. If further amplification is desirable, the alternating current from the secondary of the transformer may be delivered to the grid circuit of a second amplifying tube, as shown in Fig. 34. From the second tube it then goes to a detector tube or to a crystal detector. This method of

successively using two or more tubes for amplification
is called *cascade amplification*. The last tube in such
an amplifier of radio-frequency waves is called the detector tube, and the other tubes are called amplifier
tubes. An amplifier consisting of one detector tube and
two amplifier tubes is said to have two stages of amplification.

Instead of transferring the amplified energy by
means of a transformer coupling, the coupling may be

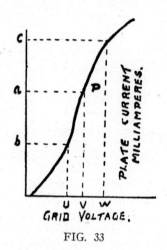

FIG. 33

simply a resistance, or may be a condenser. A circuit
using resistance coupling is shown in Fig. 35, in which
the radio-frequency power is amplified by two tubes
coupled together through resistances, and then detected.
After passing through the detector, the currents of
audio-frequency can be further amplified by one or
more audio-frequency stages. An amplifier in which

the signal is amplified *before* reaching the detector is
called a radio-frequency amplifier. An amplifier in
which the signal is amplified *after* passing through the
detector is called an audio-frequency amplifier. Resistance couplings in radio-frequency amplifiers have
been extensively used in France, but not to so great an
extent in the United States. The advantage of a resistance-coupled amplifier is that while the amplification
per tube may not be so great as with transformer

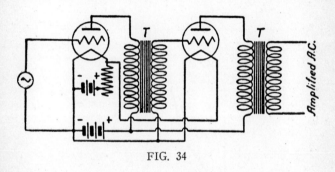

FIG. 34

couplings, the amount of amplification is practically independent of the wave length for long wave lengths.
Resistance-coupled amplifiers seldom give full amplification at wave lengths below 1,000 meters. In order
to get the greatest power output, and hence the greatest
power amplification, from a tube, a resistance should be
used in the plate circuit of a value equal to the average
internal resistance of the tube between plate and filament. In this respect the tube is similar to any other
electrical machine and to a battery. Usually, however,
such small currents flow into the detector used with
radio-frequency amplifier that the detector may be con-

sidered a voltage-operated device, in which case the maximum voltage output and not the maximum power output is desired from the amplifier tubes. This is realized by making the coupling resistances larger than the internal resistance of the tube between plate and filament, in some cases two or three times as large. These high resistances require higher plate voltages than are required for transformer coupling, perhaps voltages two or three times as great as for transformer coupling. In some cases, as in some military applications, this may be a real disadvantage.

For audio-frequency amplification, iron core transformers are used. For transformer-coupled radio-frequency amplification the small transformers used generally have air cores—that is, no iron is used. There have recently been developed radio-frequency transformers with iron cores, very thin laminations being used.

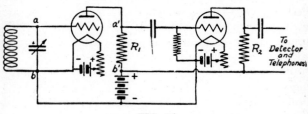

FIG. 35

THE PHOTO-ELECTRIC CELL

THE most common forms of energy are mechanical energy, heat, chemical, electrical, magnetic, sound and light energy. Some of the things we wish to do with these forms of energy are, to capture them from their natural sources, to store, transport, transmit, measure, record, observe, control, transform them into other forms of energy, and to control one form of energy by another. For example, mechanical energy exists in the form of water flowing in streams. We capture this from nature by hydraulic turbines. We store this by holding the water at an elevation in reservoirs. Mechanical energy is carried in storage by everyone who has a watch.

The effects of mechanical energy are common to observation. Its control is commonly by clutches, brakes, etc., and it controls other forms of energy by means of electrical contacts, triggers on guns, etc. That is to say, a small amount of mechanical energy applied to the trigger of a rifle controls a large amount of chemical energy. A similar story might be written about other forms of natural energy. But when we come to energy in the form of light, we find that the story is rather brief in spite of the fact that light energy is perhaps one of the most important to the human race.

Light Energy. Light energy is captured from nature almost solely by plant growth. To store it, except in minute amounts by phosphorescent chemicals, is impossible. Since it cannot be stored, it cannot be transported in storage. It transmits itself, but its measurement is a thing of considerable difficulty, and recording is even more difficult. To control its formation from

103

other forms of energy is usually relatively easy, but for it to control any other form of energy is very difficult. Its transformation into other forms of energy is greatly limited by lack of suitable means.

In this discussion of light we must not forget that light, as ordinarily accepted, is distinct from radiant heat, and hence the energy as light is really quite small. If heat be absorbed out of sunlight, the remainder is a very small amount of energy. This energy cannot be transformed into usable mechanical energy. It may be transformed into heat, but the resulting heat is very

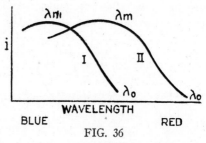

WAVELENGTH

BLUE   RED

FIG. 36

CHARACTERISTIC CURVES OF A PHOTO-ELECTRIC CELL SHOWING THE RELATION BETWEEN CURRENT AND WAVE LENGTH.

small. It is transformed into chemical energy by many natural processes of growing tissues, especially in plants. It never makes a sound, it has no magnetic effect which can be detected by ordinary magnetic detecting devices, and it is transformed from one wave length of light to another with extreme difficulty.

From this one sees that while light energy is of such great importance to the human race, the things which it can be made to do are greatly limited. It can make us see, it can be recorded by a camera and it can be transformed into electrical energy by the photo-electric cell.

The Photo-Electric Cell. How brief a recital this makes compared with the recital of electric energy, which can be transformed quickly into other forms of energy, which by simple means controls almost any form of energy, and yet which itself is by nature so infrequently applied to the human system. It is very fortunate for us that one of our first light detecting instruments—the photo-electric cell—controls so universally applicable an energy as electricity. The human race has had for many years mechanical prime movers, mechanical legs and arms, and it has had electrical

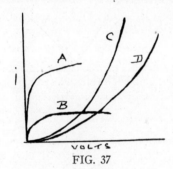

FIG. 37

CHARACTERISTIC CURVES SHOWING THE VOLTAGE CURRENT RELATIONS.

heaters, chemical heaters and so on, but the human race has been dependent upon the human eye for its detection and record of light. If the photo-electric cell can be made by a simple process to take the place of the human eye in certain places, it can be of great service to mankind.

The photo-electric processes are well known to most of us. Such processes are common in plants, and have been brought to a high degree of perfection in photographic materials, but these processes usually have a time element involved which is too long to permit their use in the quick control of things we wish done on the spur of the moment. For instance, we can arrange a camera to record the motion of a thief in a room, and that may be of assistance in tracing him after the theft has been committed and the thief has made his getaway; but how much better it would be if we had a photo-electric watchman to turn in the alarm when the thief entered the building, instead of waiting, perhaps hours, before turning in the report. It is for purposes of this kind that the photo-electric cell may be of value to us.

The Photo-Electric Effect. The photo-electric cell process is distinct from the photo-chemical process in that light and electrons alone take part in it. If a zinc plate be suspended by a silk thread and charged with electricity from a static machine, it will hold its charge for a long time. If however, the light from an arc lamp be allowed to shine upon the zinc plate, it will be found that, if the plate is charged negatively, it will lose its charge very rapidly under the action of the ultra violet light from the arc lamp; but, if the plate is charged positively, it will retain its charge quite as well when the light is allowed to shine upon the plate as when the light does not shine upon it. This simple experiment will serve to illustrate the effect known as the photo-electric effect. Since the plate loses the negative charge, but not the positive, it is evident that the light causes the zinc to release electrons which are expelled from the zinc by its negative charge, just as heating the filament in a vacuum tube allows the filament to release electrons.

Different metals than zinc will also release electrons when the light shines upon them. Experiments have shown that the light most powerful in its ability to release electrons from metals is the light of highest frequency, that is violet or ultra violet. The common metals such as iron, copper, gold and platinum will release electrons only under the action of strong light in

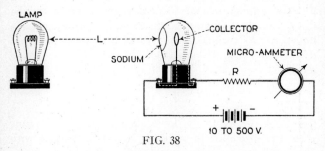

FIG. 38

Arrangement of Photo-Electric Cell in Circuit as a Photometer.

the extreme ultra violet; whereas experiment has also shown that certain of the metals, such as sodium and potassium, will release electrons under the action of visible light. The difference in the willingness of the various metals to release electrons is probably in part responsible for their chemical activity. It is quite evident that gold and platinum are less active chemically than zinc, and in the same way zinc is less active chemically than are sodium and potassium. In fact, sodium and potassium are so active they cannot be kept in the atmosphere without quickly combining with the oxygen and the water vapor of the atmosphere, and this combination renders their surface insensitive photo-electrically to visible light. It is for these reasons that photo-electric cells are made of sodium, potassium or similar metals and are made in the form of vacuum tubes, so that their surface may be preserved from chemical combination which will impair its photo-electric sensitiveness.

Uses to Which a Photo-Electric Cell Can Be Put. In the use of photo-electric cells we have four variables; they are light energy, wave length or color, applied voltage, and current. Fig. 36 shows the relation between current and wave-length. Curve 1 is for a light atomic weight alkali like sodium or lithium, and II for a heavier atomic weight material such as potassium and rubidium. λ_o is in each the long wave length limit and λ_m is the wave-length at which maximum current is delivered. This curve is the result of a number of phenomena, including the velocities considered last time, and also absorption coefficients for the different wave lengths. Value of λ_m given by experiment on certain cells is as follows:

Lithium	4050A°
Sodium	4190A°
Potassium	4400A°
Rubidium	4730A°
Caesium	5390A°

For convenience of engineers, let it here be explained that one inch equals 2.54 centimeters; one centimeter equals 10 millimeters, equals 10,000μ, equals $10^7\mu\mu$, equals 10^8 A° and A° is the symbol for Angstrom. These are all used as units of wave-length, but there should be no confusion because they are all multiples of ten of the standard centimeter length.

Fig. 37 is the voltage current relation. *A* is a vacuum type cell at high illumination and *B* is a vacuum type cell at about one-third this illumination. These curves are similar in shape, only differing in height over a range of at least 10,000 fold in light intensity. Curves *C* and *D* are similar curves for a gas cell; at higher voltages the cell is unstable and likely to arc.

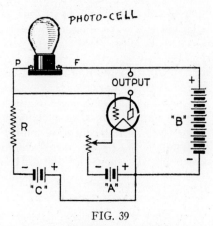

FIG. 39

CIRCUIT FOR PHOTO-ELECTRIC CELL TO BE USED WITH AN AMPLIFIER.

Uses for Photo-Electric Cell. Having such a photo-electric cell, what can it be used for?

At the present time it seems as if the photo-electric cell might prove useful for the same things that the human eyes are used, and many things that the eye cannot be used for.   Many things have been suggested, but the surface has hardly been scratched.   Photo-cells are suggested for—

Counting and timing of passing objects, transmission of speech and signals over a beam of light, sunshine detector, sign control and illumination control, burglar

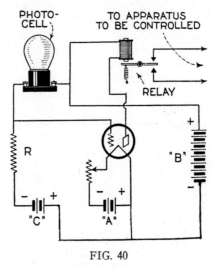

FIG. 40

Photo-Electric Circuit as Used in Connection with a Control Relay.

alarm, storm detector, measuring photographic plates and spectograms, transmission of pictures by wire and wireless picture movies, reading common print to the blind, photometry, pyrometry, registering smoke, measuring gas chart, control of lighthouses and light buoys, ultra violet light houses, ultra violet burglar alarms, sorting objects by color, talking motion pictures and phonographs.

We will now proceed to take up a few of these in brief detail:

Counting and Timing of Passing Objects. Such for instance as the counting of automobiles passing through a tunnel or by a given intersection; or the counting of a certain type of carton passing down an endless belt in a manufacturer's packing room, or the timing of races from the fastest to the slowest, or the measurement of the muzzle velocity of a projectile; these are all done in a similar way. A beam of light is thrown into the photo-electric cell causing the current to flow. When an object passes, the light is interrupted and the interruption of the current allows the relay to close which registers the time of the count.

Transmission of Speech and Signals Over a Beam of Light. If a shutter is placed in a searchlight beam, and the searchlight is aimed at a photo-electric cell, the shutter may be operated in the form of telegraphic code, and the photo-electric cell will respond to the light impulses giving electric impulses which can be recorded. The light from the searchlight beam can be made invisible by passing it through an ultra violet filter. Speech may be transmitted in this way by causing the light from the searchlight beam to vary in accordance with the voice currents in a telephone line. The resultant variations picked up by the photo-electric cell are translated into audio currents.

Sunshine Detector. This is probably the simplest use of a photo-electric cell. Nothing is required but a sensitive meter and batteries. When the sun shines brightly on a photo-cell, the battery will be permitted to send a large current through the meter. When darkness comes the current through the meter will cease. This can be easily applied to recording instruments, or it may operate a relay controlling an electric sign, or an illumination system, so that should the amount of sunshine drop below a certain value, the signs or illumination would automatically turn on.

Storm Detectors. These can be made by a simple extension of this idea. The photo-electric cell may be placed at the end of a long, black tube and aimed at that part of the sky which grows black when a storm is brewing. A relay and bell then give warning of an approaching storm, or in localities where storms come from many directions, the black tube and photo-cell could be mounted on a weather vane so that it would always point to windward. A similar application is the burglar alarm in which an automobile spot light is placed in one part of the room and its beam reflected back and forth by mirrors until it has traveled in the form of a lattice across doorways and windows, it is finally reflected by the last mirror into a box containing a photo-electric cell. Light shining upon this photo-electric cell holds a balanced relay from turning in the alarm; should the light become stronger or weaker the alarm will respond. If a burglar enters the building he must pass through at least one beam of light and that is sufficient to turn in the alarm. If he tries to fool the alarm by putting his flashlight in, it will set off the alarm. Smoke from a smoldering fire will likewise set it off. This device may also be made invisible by the use of ultra violet filters.

Measuring Photographic Plates and Spectograms. This requires only a sensitive recording instrument, a source of light and a slit. Such devices are extremely useful because the line characteristics in the spectogram is translated into an enlarged curve of density on which the maxima and minima are easily located.

Transmission of Pictures by Wire and Wireless. In this process the photograph is curled in the form of a cylinder being caused to rotate like the cylinder in a cylinder phonograph. A stationery beam of light travels over this film in the form of a spiral the same as the needle travels over the cylinder record of a dictaphone. The light passing through the photograph varies in intensity as the light and darkness of the photograph itself. The photo-electric cell responds to this light and darkness with varying current which variation is transmitted by wire or wireless to the receiving station where it causes a photographic negative to be exposed as it travels in a synchronous path before the varying light.

Television is an extension of this process, and involves primarily the transmission of sixteen such pictures per second. Many different schemes are used but they are all basicly quite similar. To consider this briefly, let us make a few assumptions, and see where they lead us to.

We will assume the following: Each picture to be transmitted is ¾ inch by one inch, sixteen of these are to be transmitted in one second, and a revolution of 1/100 of an inch is desirable. This means that our individual pictures can be divided into squares 1/100th of an inch on each side. In each picture there will be then 75 times 100 or 7,500 of such squares; sixteen of these a second will mean 120,000 per second. Now it is quite obvious that to transmit as many as 120,000 variations in one second will require very quickly responding electric circuits, detectors, amplifiers and lights, if it is all to be done by one photo-electric cell and one transmission circuit. Another scheme would be to have one hundred photo-electric cells each transmit one of the 100 squares across the film; then each one would have to transmit only 1,200 impulses in each second, but the cost of one hundred such transmitters would be out of the question. The final solution will probably be a compromise between these two. There is no difficulty with a photo-electric cell because it will probably respond to frequencies of one to sixteen million, it being a pure electron discharge in a high vacuum tube of extremely low capacity. From this we see that for quickness of response a photo-electric cell is faster than the human eye by a million times. Outside of circuit difficulties, the greatest obstacle to television is to get sufficient illumination and make it respond to the frequency. The gas discharge lamps will respond to high frequency but their illumination is very low. An incandescent filament is, of course, out of the question, as it scarcely shows a flicker in 120 vibrations per second. The arc lamp will only respond to slightly higher frequency. A possible solution is found in the polarized light magneto optic shutter.

Reading Common Print to the Blind. If light from a written page is focused by a lens upon a row of photo-cells, and each photo-cell is connected to an audio-frequency oscillating circuit of a different pitch, then this arrangement may be drawn across a printed line of common type, and as each letter is passed over different chords will be sounded in different orders for each letter passed over. The result is that a blind person can have a book read to him by such a device.

Photometry. Photo-electric cells are used for measuring the illumination in the calibration of incandescent lamps, in measuring the illumination in rooms, and in picture studios. The equipment is similar to that suggested for sunlight recording.

Pyrometry is the measurement of temperature by visible radiation and is accomplished by a similar method as photometry.

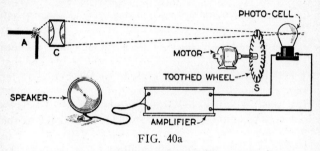

FIG. 40a

AN INTERESTING ARRANGEMENT FOR PRODUCING AUDIO FREQUENCY NOTES.

Registering Smoke Passing Up a Chimney. This is accomplished by placing a constant source of light on one side of the chimney and recording the amount of that light which arrives at the photo-electric cell on the opposite side.

Control of lighthouses and light buoys is simply an adaptation of the system used in controlling signs and illumination. In connection with lighthouses, since the photo-electric cell is sensitive to light which is outside of the visible range, it is possible that uses may develop in which lighthouses send out invisible light which will penetrate fog better than visible light will, and this will be detected by photo-electric cells instead of by eye.

Sorting Objects by Color. In sorting of yarns, cigars and other things by color, a group of photo-electric cells are used, each with its appropriate color filter. The response of these photo-cells controls the sorting mechanism.

Talking Motion Pictures and Photo-electric Phonographs. The record of speech may be recorded on the same film as that on which the motion picture is taken by using a microphone, amplifier and gas discharge tube to expose the photographic film. When this is developed and printed the result is automatic synchronizing of the voice and picture record. While the picture is being projected light passing through the voice record into a photo-electric cell translates it into electric current which amplified will operate a loud speaker. The photo-electric phonograph is simply talking film without the movie. It is obvious that there can be no needle scratch when the needle is a beam of light.

Gas Type Photo-Cells. In the gas type photo-cell, electrons are released from the sodium surface and accelerated by the applied voltage until they have such high velocity that upon collision with an atom of gas they ionize the atom; that is they break the binding force between the atom and one of its electrons, and the field then pulls the ionized atom back to the surface from which the electron came, while the newly released electron proceeds in the same direction as the colliding electron. This process may repeat itself many times and of course all this increases the current, but when the positive ion formed reaches sufficiently high velocity to cause ionization, then an arc is formed and no light is required in order that the cell pass a current. Furthermore, the current must be limited by an external resistance, otherwise the cell will be damaged if an arc should accidentally occur, due to a fluctuation in voltage.

The ionized atoms of all but a few rare gases are chemically very active, hence it is necessary in making gas type photo-cells to have extreme purity of gas, otherwise the gas will combine with the surface and the result will be a lack of constancy in the cell itself.

Even in vacuum type photo-cells it is necessary for the maker to use great precaution to get every trace of gas out of the metal before the cell is sealed, as all depends on the surface, and these photo-electric surfaces are very sensitive to contamination; being made of elements having extreme chemical activity.

Adaptations of Photo-Cells. To use a photo-cell as a photometer; that is to measure the candle power of various incandescent lights—connect as shown in Fig. 38.

The battery voltage depends upon the type of cell. For vacuum photo-cells it may be from 10 to 500 volts; 90 volts being convenient and satisfactory. Note that the negative terminal of the battery is connected to the sodium, while the positive terminal is connected to the collector. The distance L should be kept constant. The meter should have a sensitivity of about 20 microamperes for full scale. When weaker lights are to be measured, the circuit is the same, but a current sensitive galvanometer should be substituted for the microammeter, and when very weak light, like star light, is to be measured, an electro-meter and guard rings are used.

The same circuit is used with a glass photo-cell for measuring light for photographic purposes, or for measuring and recording sunlight.

When ultra-violet is to be measured, a quartz photo-cell is substituted for the glass cell. Remember that the sensitivity curve of a photo-cell is more like that of a photographic plate than the eye, hence, if lights are of different types they should not be compared on this basis alone.

With a vacuum cell no resistance is required at R, as indicated in Figs. 38, 39 and 40, but with a gas filled cell, the resistance should be about one-half megohm. The voltage is critical and must be accurately set and held constant. If the light is pulsating rapidly the output may be put through a transformer amplifier, but if slowly changing phenomena is to be studied, the amplifier must be resistance coupled.

When the photo-cell is to be used with an amplifier it should be connected as in Fig. 39. The input of the amplifier connects to the output terminals shown.

Fig. 40 A shows an interesting toy developed by Dr. R. C. Burt and now on exhibition at Washington.

A is an arc lamp, C is a condenser which throws light on a motor-driven toothed wheel at S. The photo-current is amplified and applied to the loud speaker. With the wheel stopped the arc is lighted and the loud speaker gives the audible rendition of the flickering start. When the motor is started, the pitch of the tone goes up the scale finally going beyond the range of the amplifier and loud speaker. A puff of smoke or a shadow will diminish the sound enormously. The same wave which is used in the loud speaker may be analyzed by an oscilloscope; thus giving a visual picture of the wave form at the same time its tone quality is heard. A great variety of tone quality is possible with various shaped holes in the toothed wheel.

The same circuit shown in Fig. 39 is used with a relay (see Fig. 40) and counting device or chronograph for counting or timing passing objects. It is also used with an amplifier for transmission of signal and speech over a beam of light. Either of these two circuits with the appropriate auxiliary equipment may be used for electric sign control and illumination control, burglar alarm, or storm detection.

For some problems the new grid glow tube is desirable. No general connections can be given because each case is unique in itself. From the examples already given it should not be difficult to make application of the photo-cell to specific problems.

LIGHT SENSITIVE CELLS

THERE are three known types of light sensitive cells, which are classified as follows: (1) photo-electric, (2) actino-electric, and (3) photo-voltaic. Until recently, all of the textbooks and the contributors to the science of light action on the metals were accustomed to call any electrical effect as the result of light a "photo-electric effect."

Any electrical change in an element, compound or substance resulting from light exposure thereon, was termed a photo-electric effect.

In the last few years, the literature became so abundant and replete with the various types and kinds of cells and compounds that would change in its electrical characteristics with light exposure, that it became a science by itself.

The distinctions among these three types of light sensitive devices are basic and significant, and are thoroughly worth understanding.

The Photo-Electric Effect. This is a film of an alkali metal deposited on the inside of a highly evacuated glass bulb, into which has been sealed two electrodes. One of the electrodes is termed the cathode, and consists of a film of the alkali metal or the corresponding hybride, to which we will refer later on; the other is termed the anode, better known as the collector.

If we connect a source of direct current in series with the cell and a meter—the cathode being connected with the negative terminal of the source of the current, and the collector with the positive terminal of the source of the current—on exposing the cell to a source of light, the current flows through the circuit and gives a reading on the meter. The meter reading is directly proportional to the source of light it is exposed to.

Immediately the light source is shut off, the current flow through the circuit will cease to flow as well. In fact, relationship between the light exposure and the

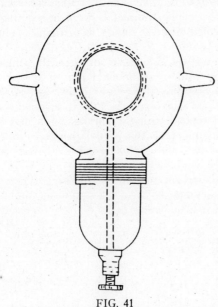

FIG. 41

TYPES OF PHOTO-ELECTRIC CELL.

current flow with respect to time is so fast that it will follow almost any speed, or rapidity of change, and can be used for any practical or laboratory purpose.

We can secure a flow of electrons between the cathode and anode much in the same fashion as with a radio tube. In the radio tube the electron flow is set up only when the filament is connected to a source of current. In the photo-electric cell a current flow occurs only on exposing the cell to a source of light, whether the cell is connected to a source of current or not.

The Actino-Electric Effect. Various special materials of a high electrical resistance give rise to the actino-electric effect. When such materials are connected in series with a source of current and a meter and are exposed to a source of light, the resistance of the material changes with the light.

An illustration of varying resistance is the well-known resistance box which is commonly used with motors. Its resistance is increased or decreased by cutting off more or less of the resistance coils in the box by passing the control switch over the multiplicity of contacts connected with the resistance coils. As the resistance is varied we may increase or decrease the speed of a motor.

The same phenomena on an entirely different scale is found with the actino-electric effect, the resistance of the material involved changing with the light reflected upon it. It might be said for completeness sake that the currents dealt with in actino-electric cells are very small indeed, and cannot be made to directly increase or decrease the speed of motors.

The Photo-Voltaic Effect. Here we have two metals inserted in a solution (electrolyte). A potential is generated on exposing one of the elements or the electrolyte to a light source. It is virtually a light sensitive battery in its most elementary form.

The technical literature shows various types and

kinds of photo-electric cells, but the forms of cells are not important to the facts given here. The reason for the different forms of cell construction is because of the different conditions that the manufacturers of cells work under. However, the shapes of the various cells play no part in their physical characteristics.

The qualities of the glassware used in the construction of cells are in regard to (1) the resistance to chemical corrosion, (2) dielectric capacity, (3) light transmission characteristics, and (4) the ease of mechanical working.

As to the first point, it is desirable that the material

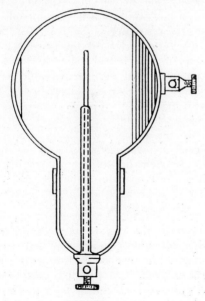

FIG. 41a

will resist contamination by the active metal deposited
on its wall; in other words, no chemical reaction must
take place between the glass and the metal deposited
thereon.   By dielectric capacity, we refer to a glass
having a high electrical resistance, thus eliminating to
a great extent "current leakage" across the terminals.

The absorption of light through the glass must be
minimized, especially so for the higher radiations, i.e.,
from the yellow lines up to the ultra violet lines in the
spectrum; therefore, one is able to cover visible and
invisible range in the cell sensitivity.   And last but not
least, the glass must be such as to permit its ease of
manufacture.

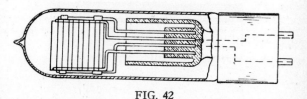

FIG. 42

THE WEIN CELL. THE LIGHT SENSITIVE MATERIAL IS DEPOS-
ITED ON A NICKEL PLATE, INSTEAD OF THE INNER GLASS WALL.

The materials most frequently employed for the
manufacture of photo-electric cells are (1) lime, (2)
Pyrex, and (3) quartz.   The last named glass is by
far the most difficult to work with, requiring a much
hotter flame by the glass-blower.   Another fact is that
it requires platinum contacts sealed through the glass
for contacts.   It must be said, however, that it is by
far the best kind of glass for photo-electric cells, since
it permits most of the actinic light to pass through it.
Quartz is quite expensive.

Pyrex is less difficult to work with, and accordingly is used extensively for commercial photo-electric cells. A less hot flame is employed for Pyrex than for quartz glass, and special kinds of sealing-in wires are used as contacts, such as tungsten, etc. Lime glass is used extensively for commercial forms of photo-electric cells. In this glass we use "copper-clad" wires for sealing in. The light transmission value of lime glass is lower than that of Pyrex, but it is readily worked in glass-blowing machines and hence is used extensively.

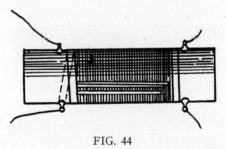

FIG. 44

AN INSULATING TUBE WITH TWO WIRES EMBEDDED IN THE GROOVES, AND THE SELENIUM BRIDGED OVER THE WIRES.

The lead wires are first fused through the glass selected and serve as the electrodes in the cell proper. The cell is then connected into a high vacuum system usually consisting of a mercury "aspirator" and an oil pump, both working in tandem. To this vacuum system is connected means for absorbing vapors generated by the oil and mercury vapor pumps.

Simultaneously with the evacuation of the bulb proper, a "degassification process" to dispose of the gases that might be in the glass and in the metal parts of the embryo cell is carried on. This process is accomplished by heating the bulb in a closed hot chamber and the metal parts by means of an "induction furnace." In this manner is secured what is termed a "hard vacuum."

The next step is to make a conducting surface on the inside of the glass bulb. The common practice is to precipitate a film of silver on the glass, much in the same fashion as is done in mirror making. In recent years this method has been dispensed with since the silver film oxidizes readily under the process of degassification.

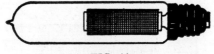

FIG. 46

The Cell Shown in Fig. 44 Placed in an Evacuated Bulb To Eliminate Atmospheric Changes.

The modern practice is to deposit a film of magnesium on the inside of the glass tube. This is usually done by "exploding" the magnesium in the evacuated bulb, following the same procedure of radio tube manufacture.

Onto the film of silver or magnesium is deposited a thin film of any of the following metals, listed according to their sensitivity: lithium, sodium, potassium, rubidium, and caesium. Other metals and alloys of metals may be used, but the foregoing are most sensitive.

After the coating of the metal has been successfully carried out, the cell is sealed off and allowed to age for several days before it is used.

For some special purposes, when cells that will respond to weaker light sources are required, special processes are used to increase the sensitivity of the deposited metal to light. This is usually done after the metal has been deposited by permitting dry hydrogen to flow through the tube and passing a discharge between the anode and cathode.

The voltages used range anywhere between 200 and 550 volts. As a result, the deposited film forms a compound with the hydrogen; for instance, in the case of potassium, it is converted into potassium hydride. The

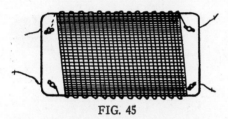

FIG. 45

A Cell in a Semi-Flat (Bifilar) Form.

film becomes colored as a result of the process. The hydrogen is evacuated and replaced by a small amount of any of the following gases: neon, argon, helium, krypton, or xenon.

What happens in the conversion process is this: the deposited film is in a very fine crystalline state (the surface); i.e., in a colloidal form. The electrons are more readily disassociated than when the active metal is not converted into the corresponding hydride.

In the case of the gases referred to, we take advantage of the conducting properties of the gas in the cell. After an electron has been released from the surface it collides against the gas, and thus amplifies itself in the cell proper, prior to its reaching the electrical amplifying circuit.

Because of its dependability, and the modern amplifying circuits, the photo-electric cell is used extensively in talking motion pictures.

The actino and photo-voltaic cells are not yet widely used even in experimental work on talking pictures, but they present interesting and promising possibilities.

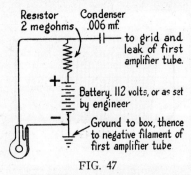

FIG. 47

ELECTRICAL CONNECTIONS OF THE PHOTO-ELECTRICAL CELL USED IN MOVIETONE.

The photo-voltaic effect is the least known among light-sensitive phenomena and has received the least attention of investigators and experimenters. This is due primarily to the fact that this particular phenomenon is very little understood, by comparison with other light-sensitive actions.

Becquerel, who first discovered the photographic effect of radio-active materials, in the middle of the last century found out that if two Daguerreotype plates were immersed in a trough of water, and if the plates were directly connected to a galvanometer, if one of the plates were exposed to a source of light—the other being dark—a deflection on the meter would be recorded, showing that a potential (current) was generated. In honor of the discoverer of this phenomenon the effect is sometimes called the "Becquerel effect" as well as the photo-voltaic effect.

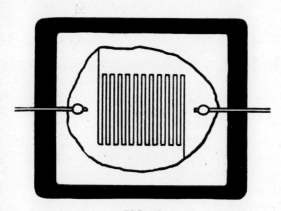

FIG. 48

PLATINUM DEPOSITED ON GLASS PLATE AND DIVIDED AS SHOWN. SILENIUM IS BRIDGED OVER DIVIDING LINES.

On close examination of this phenomenon one will observe that there really is a light-sensitive battery in its most elemental form. In other words, on exposing one of the elements in the cell a source of current is generated; and if no light is permitted upon one of the plates, no current is generated. Here we have a chemical action taking place between the plates as a result of light exposure on one of them, and as a result of this chemical action a source of current being generated which is readable on a meter.

Since the discovery of this effect a great number of contributions have been made to the knowledge of photo-chemistry, but this is only of an academic nature and of no present practical consequence. Various metals and combinations of metals, as well as alloys, have been tried, including various electrolytes (solutions), which have been recommended from time to time. These metals and electrolytes give rise to different characteristics natural to the metal and electrolyte used.

The photo-voltaic effect is different from the photo-electric effect in that with the first-named a source of current is generated as a result of light, requiring no extraneous sources of current to actuate external devices; whereas, with the second type of cell we have a different sort of action, i.e., a source of electrons being thrown or torn off from the surface of the cell as a result of light exposure. In this latter case (photo-electric), a source of potential is always required in its circuit.

Silver plates or foils have been employed with success. The surface of the metal is usually converted into a salt, a form of hypersensitizing, such as the corresponding sulphide, bromide, chloride, iodide, or oxide. The solutions found to give the best results are potassium bromide, chloride, iodide, sulphate and barium nitrate. A number of dyes have been found which function very nicely with these silver plates, among these being eosine, fluroescein, rhodamine, etc. In some instances, alcohol, acetone, glycerine and other solvents have been found to be as satisfactory as water, the electrolyte.

If two aluminum plates are inserted in acetone, and if one of these plates is coated with selenium, it will be found to give a good sensitivity to light. Instead of aluminum plates, those of platinum are found to give better results. The film of selenium must be even throughout.

The magnitude of current available from the older forms of photo-voltaic cells is very small indeed, so much so that extremely sensitive meters were used to measure these minute currents resulting from light exposure on the plates.

The photo-voltaic cell is fast becoming a popular light-sensitive cell with workers in the talking motion picture field, in the wire and radio transmission of pic-

FIG. 49

THE METAL FILM IS DIVIDED IN A CIRCULAR FORM.

tures (television), and for actuating electrical circuits by means of a ray of light.

In the year 1817 Willoughby Smith, an English telegraph operator, was desirous of securing a non-inductive, high resistance material to use with a system of cable telegraphy. The element "selenium" was recommended.

Smith took little rods of selenium to which were connected wires at each end. These rods were then placed into glass tubes which were in turn placed in a darkened box. The electrical resistance of these rods was 1,400 megohms. During his experiments, Smith took off the cover of the box containing the crude "selenium cells" and was surprised to note that each time he did so the resistance of the little selenium rods changed.

This remarkable discovery was soon described in technical periodicals the world over, and it was the subject of much discussion among physicists and experimenters. It should be noted here that the element selenium was the first light-sensitive cell known.

The actino-electric effect is characterized from the other types of light-sensitive cells by the fact that it changes its ohmic value (resistance) with light; and as an analogous illustration, it virtually does what the "starting box" does, the difference being that the resistance is changed by light and not manually, as is the rheostat.

The number of elements and compounds that exhibit the actino-electric effect is very large indeed, and we will describe here only those of the better-known types.

In view of the fact that selenium has such a very high resistance and in order that it can be made into adaptable electrical circuits, it is necessary that the selenium be spread out into extremely thin films and on a large cross sectional area within a small defined space. This is readily accomplished by the now common forms of selenium cell constructions.

The simplest form of cell construction is to wind two wires on an insulating material such as porcelain, lava, mica, etc., with the selenium being applied over these

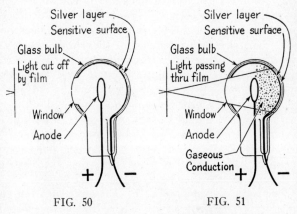

FIG. 50

Action of Photo-Electric Cell Light Cut Off by the Film Stopping Flow of Current.

FIG. 51

Light Entering Cell Through Film Allowing the Current To Flow.

two wires. In Fig. 44 is seen the cell in the form of a tube; in Fig. 45 the cell form is flat; and in Fig. 46 we see the tube form affixed in an evacuated tube.

Other forms of cell construction are obvious, as, for example, when a thin gauge of metal is sandwiched in between two insulating materials of similar size.

By far the best construction is that form known as the "grating type." It is made by depositing a film of metal, e.g., platinum or gold, on a glass plate, and thereafter dividing the film into two electrical portions in the form of a zig-zag or circular active form, as is shown in Figs. 48 and 49.

The early workers with talking motion pictures and the kindred arts were accustomed to use the selenium cell, the main reason for this being that it was readily made by almost anyone and cost very little to make. One of the main reasons why the selenium cell was discarded was because of the "inertia" period which is characteristic of this type of cell. By inertia is meant the peculiar property of the cell in requiring time to come back to its original electrical resistance prior to its being exposed to a source of light. Various electrical circuits and devices have been designed to overcome this inertia period, with varying degrees of success.

It is interesting to record here that the DeForest system of talking motion pictures in its present form makes use of a selenium cell of a special type, thus proving that the selenium cell is not obsolete after all.

Another form of light-sensitive cell is the thalofide cell, employed by T. W. Case, whose sound picture system is known as Movietone. Here Mr. Case uses thallium oxysulphide, a compound made between the reaction products of thallium and sulphide. In the early days of the Phonofilm, Dr. DeForest made use of this type of light-sensitive cell, but it was soon discarded because the thallium oxysulphide changed, chemically, in time to thallium sulphate, which latter compound was unfit for further use, since it was insensitive to light in that form. So as to minimize this slow chemical action Case has placed a colored screen over the cell form, which procedure has increased the life of the cell considerably.

The Molybdenite Cell. This compound is the result of chemical action between Molybdenum and sulphur; either the natural form, known as molybdenite, a native mineral, or the synthetic form can be used as a light-sensitive cell. It is patented by Dr. W. W. Coblentz of the U. S. Bureau of Standards.

The molybdenite cell exhibits a far less inertia period than does the selenium cell. The simplest cell design of this kind is to secure a thin lamina (crystal), and fasten two wires at opposite ends, and by means of a soft solder be made to hold very rigidly.

STUDIO TECHNIQUE

There are three kinds of sound pictures. One is the regular feature movie, of which all or part of the dialogue is "talkie." Then there is the "short"—a song, instrumental number, or dialogue, serious or funny, lasting for a few minutes. The third is merely the synchronization of a musical score with the silent film, or the addition of some sound effects.

A number of producers are still making the movie feature all silent. When the silent film is finished its sound possibilities are studied, and in consultation with the sound director certain scenes may be scheduled for talking or sound effects. The sounds may be only the barking of a dog, a scream in the night, a pistol shot or a rushing train. So the scene of the feature we are going to witness is merely the retaking for dialogue or sound effects of a silent picture that has already been completed.

The action on the stage is observed by a man in a room next door. This man, the monitor, is one of the new powers that sound pictures have brought into being. He occupies all alone a great chamber that in one studio measures precisely 57 feet long by 44 feet wide and 35 feet high. It is the necessity of this lonely individual occupying a room large enough to hold a hundred men that brings forcefully to mind the delicacy of the sound problems in this synthetic art.

The monitor's room is shut off from the outside by double walls, so that no undesirable sounds penetrate to it. Looking down onto the stage through three thicknesses of glass, the monitor watches the action, and by

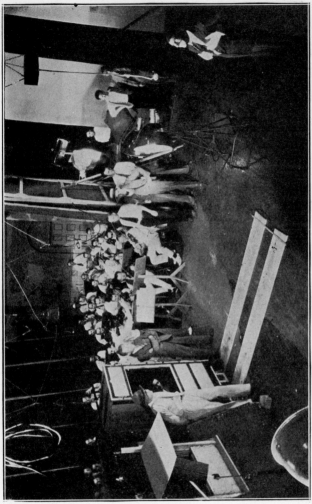

FIG. 55

A Scene in Warner Bros. Studio During the Making of
the "Singing Fool."

a loud-speaker connected directly to the stage he hears
all the sounds that go to the recording device. In front
of him is a large instrument with a set of dials. Each
dial is the control for the volume of sound that is to
be transmitted to the recorder for each microphone on
the stage. Like a cook, therefore, the monitor can mix
the sounds on this mixer panel so as to produce the
sauce that he thinks most appropriate.

He may, at his judgment, if an orchestra is playing,
tone down the volume coming from the microphones

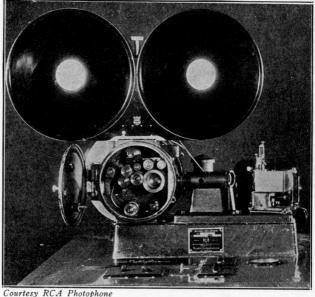

Courtesy RCA Photophone

FIG. 56

RCA SOUND RECORDER.

over the enthusiastic violinists and at the same time increase the volume from the tired or indifferent brass players. If a number of actors are on the set he can increase or reduce the volume of each one's voice. He

Courtesy RCA Photophone

FIG. 57

RCA RECORDING EQUIPMENT, LEFT TO RIGHT: RECORDER (STORAGE BATTERIES UNDER TABLE). RECORDER AMPLIFIER (MIXING PANEL, GAIN CONTROLS). MICROPHONE AMPLIFYING BOX IN FOREGROUND; MICROPHONE.

can change an assailed maiden's shriek to a squeak, or raise the weary villain's whispered threats to a terrifying, threatening boom. He can vary the volume of the basso's profound intonations and increase or decrease the thunder of the crescendo that a conductor is endeavoring to draw from his orchestra.

Courtesy of Bell Telephone Laboratories

FIG. 58

VIEW SHOWING TWO OF THE DISC RECORD RECORDING MACHINES.

It is the monitor, too, who often sends by telephone the order to stop the action if he hears some untoward sound coming from the stage. He may remind the elaborately dressed actress that the rustle of her

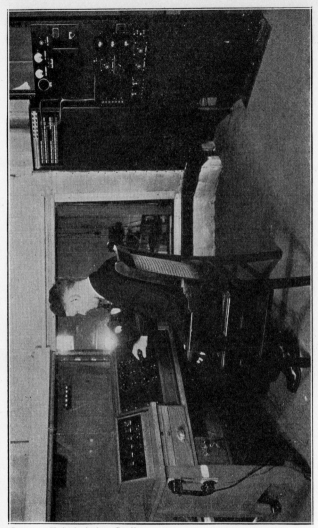

FIG. 60

VIEW OF "MIXING ROOM" SHOWING A DISTRIBUTOR AND AMPLI-
FIER PANEL ON RIGHT. THE OPERATOR AT MONITOR CONTROL
GOVERNS THE VOLUME AND MESHES THE VOICE AND MUSIC
WITH THE FILM.

dresses sounds like a hailstorm, or that the handsome hero's shoes squeak.

To make the room soundproof is easy. The concrete construction and double walls do that. But to kill echoes and vibrations is the problem that is keeping the sound experts, these new powers in moviedom, awake nights. Science, however, has been solving the

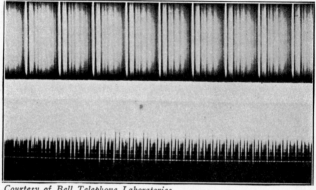

Courtesy of Bell Telephone Laboratories

FIG. 59

Photographic Records of Sound May be Either of Constant Width and Varying Density, Shown Above, or of Constant Density and Varying Width as Shown Below.

problem. By composing the inner wall of a number of different materials selected for their sound-absorbing qualities, they have been able to kill 50 per cent of the sound waves in nine-tenths of a second. One of the materials used on the wall is a specially prepared felt. The other elusive 50 per cent of your sounds is what the engineers are gunning for. Even the floor and ceiling are made of special preparations. Furthermore, the stage floor is not connected with the walls, and is itself made of a number of layers of various materials. The top layer may be cork, or even a heavy carpet which will deaden footsteps.

On the stage are two camera booths, both encased within soundproof compartments and wheeled onto the stage on rubber wheels. One compartment has two cameras for long shots and for closeups, and the other holds a single camera for angle shots.

Above the stage, suspended from wires, are a number of microphones which catch the sounds from various parts of the stage and transmit them to the sound-recording devices. The usual stage paraphernalia or sets and lighting equipment is all ready. In some of the more advanced studios special microphones labeled "M" are used exclusively for transmitting the male voice, and others labeled "F" to record the delicate shades contained in women's voices.

There has been in progress on the stage a conference of the various experts—the sound director, the lighting director, the scenarist, cameraman, the director and, not to be forgotten, the actors. The various effects to be obtained are discussed, the cues are settled upon, and the actors take their places.

Then follows a period of communication between the various parts of this movie organism. The cameramen have gone into their booth and signify by flashing a light on to the stage that their film is threaded and that they are ready. The sound director on the stage telephones to a man in a room which overlooks the stage, and he, too, signifies he is ready. In the sound-recording room, where the sound-recording devices are installed, is a man also at a telephone receiver, and he is

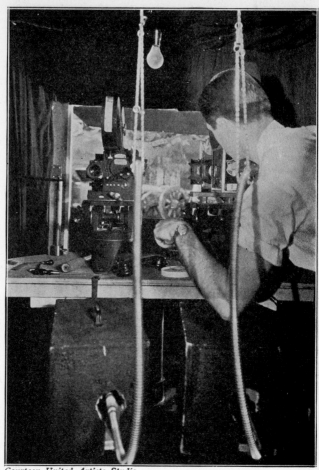

FIG. 61

VIEW OF CAMERA BOOTH. THE CAMERAS ARE MOTOR DRIVEN
AND ARE ENCLOSED IN THE METAL CASES SHOWN BELOW THE
BENCH. THEY ARE DRIVEN BY THE FLEXIBLE SHAFTS.

ordered to get his apparatus ready. This, too, for the amplifying room, where the sounds are amplified to give a power sufficient to operate the recording apparatus.

To decide whether the final sound record is to be

Courtesy of Bell Telephone Laboratories

FIG. 62

A SOUND RECORDER.

made on a disc or record, or on the edge of the film itself (as in the sound track method), a test record of the scene is first made on the disc. This is to permit the record to be played back immediately after the scene is over so that the actual sound effects may be known.

The record used is made of wax, its surface being ground at the studio to a mirror-like polish.

By the flashing of signal lights on the stage, the various parts of this organism have signified that they are ready. Then, at a final signal from the director, the actors begin their scene, the cameraman starts his reel, the electricians switch on the power, the recorder starts revolving the disc, and like the starting of a ponderous machine the movie organism begins to function.

From the time the scene starts until it is stopped, for one reason or another, not a word is spoken except by the actors. The directors have by necessity developed a new sign language. With the waving of arms, with imploring, threatening, applauding gestures all their own they ask the actors for more or less force or emotion. The directors are acquiring the technique of an orchestra conductor. Or, to put it another way, while our well-known actors of pantomime are finding their voices and adding sound to their répertoire, the directors are losing their voices and acquiring pantomime.

Several times the scene is stopped by the sound experts on the stage or by the directors. Then everything —actors, cameras and sound discs—stops at once. Then the directors can express their opinion of the hapless actors, or they can engage in a new conference on "effects." With many starts and stops made as if by a well-oiled machine the scene proceeds through and with a final wave of his hand the director orders the "cut." Illustrating the great refinement of method necessary, and a cause of a "stop," in one studio an actor walking across the carpeted stage acquired a charge of static electricity by his scuffling gait. On reaching the microphone he accidentally touched it, thereby dis-

FIG. 63

THE AMPLIFIER RACK. THE SOUND STAGES ARE TERMED "CHANNELS" INSTEAD OF STAGES. THIS PHOTOGRAPH SHOWS THE DISTRIBUTING FRAME IN THE BACKGROUND. THE TELE-PHONIC SWITCHBOARD EFFECT PERMITS IN AND OUT CONNEC-TIONS IN ANY PART OF THE AMPLIFIER SYSTEM FOR TESTING PURPOSES, PLAY-BACK, ETC.

charging the static onto the microphone and ruining the record that was being taken.

Then there are the heartbreaking efforts to control the human element. In one "short," requiring four scenes to be taken on four different days, it developed on the third day that the actor acquired a slight, and at that time imperceptible, hoarseness. This was only detected when the act was finished and a test run of the four scenes was made. Then it was found that the continuity of the scenes was rudely disturbed by the changed voice in the third scene.

When the scene is finished then comes the "play back." The record that has just been made is played back on the stage and the effects rendered may be observed by all and criticized. Here the blue note of the musician, the falsetto of the singer, or the sneezing of an extra is unfailingly detected.

After the "play back" the directors may decide to do the scene over with another test record. And they will continue the rehearsing until they are sure they have the right effects and every one knows his part. Then and then only is the final recording made, either on the disc or on the film.

A number of miniature theatres designed to reproduce perfectly the acoustics of a modern theatre are also a part of the sound studio. Here the finished picture will be run off after the film and records have been developed, and a final criticism and editing may be accomplished under theatre conditions. It is in these theatres that the greatest ingenuity has been used to devise means to reproduce the theatre conditions. For as the sounds register in the toy theatres they will sound when they are presented to the public, which pays the bills.

For example, it has been found that the presence of an audience in a theatre will in itself change the acoustic or sound transmitting properties of the room. Each human being has a sound reflecting and absorbing property. Mathematical constants have therefore been devised for each object in the theatre, and the total sound property of the entire theatre is painstakingly worked out from these constants.

Even the supply of electricity must be of a special brand. The general city supply, it is found, has in it some static which unfits it to operate directly the sound machines. Therefore the city system is used to charge storage batteries which in turn, having strained the sound out of the electricity, will supply the necessary power.

Another room of the studio will probably be a well-guarded library of what might be termed "equivalent acoustics." These will be devices "which give sounds which when recorded sound like some other object whose sound is desired." For it has been found that many sounds when reproduced do not transmit the reality but are distorted. A barking dog or a pistol shot will not reproduce as such. Therefore some curious instruments have been devised from tin cans, pieces of string, bottles and wooden sticks, after the most painstaking labor. They are operated by an effects man, who watches the screen and at the right moment by a cue from the director does his part. The effects man is one of the valuable and necessary partners in this new and curious art. He is trying sincerely to reproduce more faithfully than nature a sound effect.

FIG. 64

THE LABORATORY TEST RACK. THIS PERMITS THE CHECKING
OF ALL ELECTRICAL PARTS OF THE "SYSTEM" SUCH AS AMPLI-
FIERS, ETC., TO ASCERTAIN IF THEY ARE SATISFACTORY. THE
CENTER PANEL SENDS OUT WHAT IS KNOWN AS "FREQUEN-
CIES" INTO THE AMPLIFIERS INDICATING JUST HOW EFFICIENT
THE AMPLIFIERS ARE AND HOW FREE FROM DISTORTION.

FIG. 66

KLIEG SIDE FLOODLIGHTS.

INCANDESCENT LIGHTING OF STUDIO SETS

FORMERLY the lighting of studio sets for motion picture photography has been accomplished, principally, with various forms of arc lamps, supplemented by a few Cooper-Hewitt tubes, and an occasional Mazda lamp, ortho-chromatic films being used almost entirely. But of late there has been a marked trend toward the use of incandescent lamps, ranging in size from 1,000 to 10,000 watts, used with special projectors.

The change from arc lamps to incandescent units has been influenced by: (1) Advent of "Talking Movies" with its sensitive sound recording instruments—imposing a restriction for absolute silence in the studio—the Mazda lamp meeting this requirement. (2) Demand for greater economy in the making of motion pictures —one of the means toward this end being to reduce the cost of lighting the set in the studio. (3) Introduction of panchromatic film, with its ability to correctly register all colors of the spectrum, and give better tone rendition—offering an improvement in the quality of the picture, and meeting the demand for greater beauty in films. (4) Spectral characteristics of the light of gas-filled Mazda lamps—with ability to bring out the finer qualities in panchromatic films.

Lighting in motion picture studios may be grouped under two classifications—general and modelling. The purpose of general lighting is to provide a ground-work illumination which is fairly uniform in intensity throughout the set, illuminating areas that other lights do not serve, and permitting control of the shadow

152

density over the entire set. The function of modelling lights is to give much higher intensity in limited areas, producing distinct high lights and shadows, modelling actors, back-lighting, cross-lighting, giving emphasis to certain parts of the set, creating depth and other special lighting effects.

The general lighting of the set is obtained with broadside and overhead units. The Broadside Units are usually grouped on both sides of the camera, and project their light horizontally to illuminate the front of the set. Various types of units are employed, such as: (1) Sun Spots—powerful projectors for general depth lighting and spotting-out and to produce strong shafts of light and sun effects, and for the very deep general lighting required on the larger sets. (2) Strip Lights —for general foreground lighting, compact and suited to be placed in confined space, frequently close to the place of action, used in lighting doorways, windows, and for vertical mounting behind posts or columns. (3) Side Lamps—for foreground, close-up, and general set lighting, and for light projection into the deeper sets. (4) Utility Lights—small units that may be hung on the wall for general utility and effect lighting.

Overhead Units are needed for the deeper sets to send light to the rear areas that cannot be illuminated satisfactorily by the broadsides. They must be capable of supplying higher illumination on the vertical than on the horizontal surfaces, and direct their light downward at an angle of 30 to 45 degrees below the horizontal.

For Modelling Lights high powered light projectors are employed, having beams of restricted areas and intensities from two to four times that of general illumination and sometimes a greater ratio. Intensity varies from 200 to 1,500 foot candles, covering areas from three to twelve feet in diameter, and projecting a distance from twelve to thirty feet or more.

Kliegl Bros. of New York, designers and manufacturers of the well known Kliegs in which the arc was employed—have developed a new form of Klieglights in which high-candle-power incandescent lamps are used for the light source—which are designed to meet present-day studio conditions.

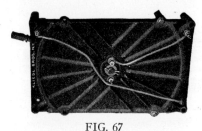

FIG. 67

5,000 Watt Dimmer.

These new Kliegs furnish brilliant evenly diffused light high in actinic qualities, permitting photography with clearness of detail, full color values, sharp definition, and freedom from sound interference. They are absolutely noiseless in operation and cause no disturbance in the recording of sound photography. They are efficient in light control and utilization; afford complete command over the direction, diffusion, and divergence of the light beam; are light in weight; can be easily and quickly handled; operate on the service line, whether AC or DC; and introduce economies in current consumption, production time, and labor requirements. Several of the principal units are herewith described.

Klieg-Sun (No. 1,144-B)—A long beam, high intensity flood-light, for projecting a strong, well-defined, evenly-diffused beam of light a considerable distance—covering a restricted area; used especially for general lighting of deep sets, producing sunlight effects, spotting-out, modelling, and for accentuating main points of interest; accommodates 2,000-, 5,000-, and 10,000-watt G type Mazda lamps; and operates on 110-120 volts, alternating or direct current.

Projector consists of a cylindrical lamp housing containing a receptacle, reflecting mirror and adjustable

FIG. 68

Klieg Mazda Lamp Adapters.

lens; mounted on a telescopic standard; set on a base fitted with ball-bearing rubber-tired casters; constructed as to minimize weight; designed to allow free and easy movements, adjustments in height, and to roll easily over the floor.

Housing, of rust-resisting Russian iron, with cast-aluminum frame front and rear, is of sufficient strength to meet all service requirements, and well ventilated to insure comparatively cool operation—thus prolonging the life of the lamps. Slide grooves on the front permit the use of a diffusing screen.

Receptacle for the lamp is mounted on a traveling base, controlled by a small lever at the rear of the housing. It moves along the reflector axis, which allows focusing the lens and regulating its beam spread from eight to approximately thirty degrees.

An adapter can be furnished to fit the lamp receptacle, permitting the use of the smaller-sized lamps than that for which the unit is designed. The adapter serves to correctly position the lamp filament in the optical axis of the reflector. A heat-resisting mirrored-glass parabolic reflector, in the rear of housing, back of the lamp, reflects the light, increased the efficiency, and facilitates control of the light beam. A six-inch piano-convex condensing lens is set in front of the bulb— mounted on a movable carriage, controlled by a small lever at the rear of the housing, equalizes the intensity of the luminous rays and eliminates "ghosts," or dark centre, which would otherwise be present when the beam is spread.

Mounting is so devised that the lamp can be balanced in any position; light beam projected in any direction; lamp raised or lowered within a range of from 5′ 9″ to 8′ 5″, or demounted for carrying aloft. A device on the yoke and hand clamps provides means for holding the projector securely in any set position.

Klieg-Sun Projectors are made in two sizes—one with a 19″ reflector, the other with a 25″ reflector; and are furnished complete with pin-plug connector, asbestos leads, and twenty-five feet of cable. A metal frame with prismatic glass can be furnished to diffuse the light. A dimmer can also be furnished mounted on the base, permitting full or gradual control of the light from black-out to full brilliancy.

Klieg Side-Floodlights (No's. 1,152-1,153)—High-intensity variable-range floodlights giving evenly-diffused light for general illumination; projecting the beam usually in a horizontal direction or at a slight

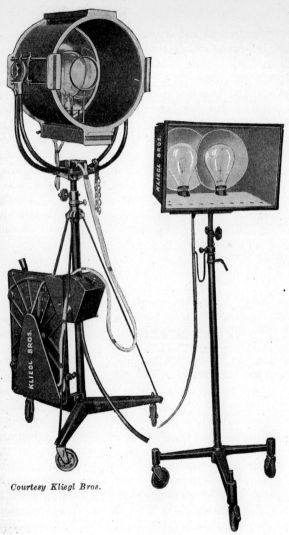

FIG. 69

KLIEG SUN PROJECTOR AND TWIN FLOODLIGHT.

angle above or below the horizontal; used as a side lamp for general lighting of deep studio-sets and close-up photography; accommodate a 1,000-, 1,500-, or 2,500-watt PS 52 Mazda lamp; operate on 110-120 volts, direct or alternating current; consist of a deep parabolic reflector 19½" in diameter, fitted with a mogul-screw-base receptacle, flexibly mounted on a telescopic pedestal, and set on a base equipped with ball-bearing rubber-tired casters; made in two designs, one with a spun-copper chromium-plated reflector, the other with a silvered-glass reflector.

No. 1,152—is equipped with the spun-copper parabolic reflector, having concentric corrugations to diffuse the light and its reflecting surface chromium plated. Lamp receptacle and toggle switch are encased in an aluminum housing mounted back of the reflector —and the reflecting unit is supported by an adjustable bracket on the telescopic pedestal stand. Head has an angular adjustment of approximately 25° either side of the horizontal; a vertical adjustment of from 4' 11" to 7' 7"; may be turned in any direction, demounted for carrying aloft, or set on a short pivot on the base close to the floor.

No. 1,153—is equipped with a silvered-glass reflector of parabolic contour and spirally rifled to control and diffuse the light; is protectively encased in sheet metal; with lamp receptacle and toggle switch enclosed in an aluminum housing back of the reflector. Reflecting unit is supported in a yoke, is perfectly balanced, can be turned in any direction, and clamped in any position. Head may be raised or lowered from 4' 8" to 6' 8", or demounted for carrying aloft. Standard and yoke are of tubular construction.

Klieg Twin Floodlight (No. 1,150)—is a wide-spread

high-intensity floodlight for general illumination, projecting an evenly-diffused light over a large area; used for lighting foregrounds, close-ups, and general lighting of studio sets; accommodates two 1,000-watt or two 1,500-watt PS 52 Mazda lamps. Projector consists of an all metal box reflector fitted with two screw-base receptacles; mounted on a telescopic pedestal, set on a base equipped with ball-bearing rubber-tired casters, and so designed as to allow variations in the projection of the light in every direction, adjustments in height, and to roll easily over the floor.

FIG. 70

DIFFUSING SCREENS.

Reflectors are of spun aluminum and are set in a deep open-front sheet-metal box. The reflector contour is parabolic, giving directional control of the light, and its reflecting surface has been chemically treated to properly diffuse the light. The receptacles are placed well toward the rear, with the lamps close to the reflector. The inside surfaces of the box casing are painted a permanent white to insure maximum reflection. Provisions have been made for ample ventilation—and slide grooves on the front permit the use of a diffusing screen.

Special bracket mounting allows angular variations in a vertical plane, and telescopic pedestal, permits head to be raised or lowered from 5' 3" to 7' 11", turned in any direction, or demounted, and set on a short pivot on the base with beam center 26" from the floor.

It is furnished complete with pedestal stand, and twenty-five feet of stage cable. A metal frame, fitted with prismatic glass, for diffusing the light can be furnished.

Klieg Overhead Floodlight (No. 1,155)—is a suspension type high-candle-power floodlight for general illumination—giving an evenly-diffused wide spread of light; projected downward at a variable angle, usually from thirty to sixty degrees below the horizontal; used as an overhead unit for lighting backgrounds, and rear areas of studio sets; accommodates one 1,000-watt or one 1,500-watt PS 52 Mazda lamp, operates on 110-120 volts, either direct or alternating current.

Projector consists of a deep parabolically-curved spun-aluminum reflector with front opening 18" in diameter, and so constructed that the central horizontal axis of the reflector is at a fixed angle of approximately thirty degrees with the horizontal axis of the lamp.

When hung this Klieglight normally projects the light downward at an angle of approximately forty-five degrees below the horizontal—and swinging support allows angular variations of approximately thirty degrees or more, either side of the normal angle.

A mogul-screw-base receptacle is mounted in an aluminum housing that projects from the top of the

reflector—air passages allow for ventilation. Centre
of the lamp filament coincides with the focal point of
the reflector and gives proper light control; and inside
surfaces of the aluminum reflector have been chemically treated to produce a proper diffusion of the light.

Courtesy Kliegl Bros.

FIG. 71

OVERHEAD FLOODLIGHT.

Pipe clamp with swivel joint, attached to the yoke, affords convenient means for suspension of the unit, and
for projecting the light in any direction.

Klieg Spotlight (No. 8N22)—A high-intensity long-
range spotlight for use with incandescent lamps; pro-

jects a concentrated beam of light any distance up to
100 ft., gives a 3-ft. spot, or a wide spread; and is used
in the studio for: back lighting—to give depth to the
picture; cross lighting— to eliminate facial shadows;
intense spotlighting; follow-up floodlighting; modelling;

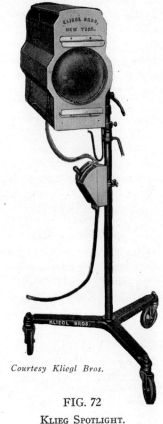

Courtesy Kliegl Bros.

FIG. 72

KLIEG SPOTLIGHT.

and for special lighting effects; accommodates a 2,000-watt concentrated filament G 48 Mazda lamp, and operates on 110-120 volts, alternating or direct current.

Spotlight is flexibly mounted on a telescopic pedestal stand; can be set at any angle, raised, lowered, or turned in any direction; and the base is fitted with casters permitting it to be rolled easily over the floor.

Lamp housing, 22-inches in length, is light-tight, thoroughly ventilated and substantially constructed—with framework of cast aluminum, and sides of rust-resisting Russian iron. It is equipped with: an eight-inch condensing lens—so supported as to allow unrestricted expansion of the glass to avoid breakage; a mogul screw-base receptacle—mounted on a sliding base, with a vertical adjustment for centring the light source, and a rod extending through the rear of the housing for focusing; a concave chromium-plated reflector—mounted back of the lamp to insure full utilization of the light source and to intensify the light beam; a large self-closing spring door—on one side of the hood which permits easy access to interior for changing lamps; and slide grooves—on the front of the hood for holding iris shutter or other devices used in obtaining special lighting effects.

Spotlight is furnished complete with telescopic stand, asbestos leads, enclosed switch, and 25 ft. of stage cable.

MOTION PICTURE CAMERAS FOR SOUND WORK

SERIOUS problems are involved in the adaptation of Motion Picture Cameras for sound work.

Such apparatus may be classed in two distinct categories—first, cameras which are simultaneously used for picture and sound recording and cameras which are used only for taking the picture record, the sound record being obtained through a separate and distinct instrument.

Cameras of the first category, of which the Bell & Howell, adopted by the Fox-Case Company, is the prototype, are used only in connection with newsreel and some exterior work and are, in our estimation, going to be discarded in the relatively near future.

A description of one of these cameras is given elsewhere in this work and we may just mention that the Fox-Case Corporation modified the Bell & Howell cameras by adapting to it the A. E. O. light and slit through which the modulated sound record is impressed upon the film while passing a point on the feed sprocket where its motion and tension are continuous and uniform.

Provision had been made for insuring the uniform, silent running of the camera at the required speed of 90 feet per minute. This was insured by the use of thirty volt direct current motors used with rheostat control operated from storage batteries, or by special spring motors for exterior work, and by synchronous motors in indoor work where the simultaneous use of more than one camera was necessary. The second category

164

of cameras are those exclusively used in studio work where they are used purely to photograph the picture record while the sound record is registered through an entirely separate unit which remains stationary and may be located at any distance from the picture recording camera.

Several cameras are generally operated for the photographing of one single scene. The cameras are all interlocked, through synchronous motors, with the sound recording apparatus. This permits the photographing of the several phases of the scene, usually expressed as long shots, semi-closeups and closeups, at the same time and synchronously with one single sound record.

The requirements of a camera suitable for photographic work in conjunction with sound recording, involve first an increase of 50% of the former standard speed of 16 pictures or one foot per second, and secondly the complete elimination of any noise which could be detected by the microphone with results so disturbing in the final reproduction as to irremediably mar the sound record.

The first problem had been happily solved a few years previous to the advent and public recognition of the sound and talking picture. As early as 1921 a speed movement had been successfully introduced by the Bell & Howell Company. In the course of the last few years, this movement was subjected to several improvements, from which resulted the well-known "check pawl super-speed movement" which required very slight modifications in the line of noise elimination to render it extremely suitable for sound picture recording.

A few considerations may be expressed here upon the most salient mechanical features of any such mechanism.

In the designing of a super-speed mechanism, it was necessary to overcome many obstacles, the greatest of which are the laws of inertia of moving objects and the overcoming of the relatively low tensile strength of the film.

Super-speed movements are generally designed so as to permit the taking of 128, and over, picture frames per second, or an increase of 8 times over the standard

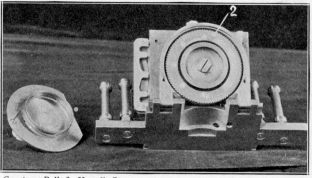

Courtesy Bell & Howell Co.

FIG. 76

CHECK PAWL SUPER SPEED MOVEMENT. NO. 2, FORMICA (FIBRE) GEAR.

normal speed. The mechanism is then required to travel through a perpendicular path and completely reverse its direction of travel 256 times per second.

Since in sound work, the standardized speed is only 24 picture frames per second, the to-and-fro motion of the mechanism is reduced to 48 times per second and the film is then accelerated from a stationary position to a speed of approximately three feet per second during its downward travel and then brought to a stationary position again, consuming only about 1/45th of a second, during which time the camera shutter is obscuring light from the film, to complete this cycle, as compared with 1/243rd of a second, which is the time

Courtesy Bell & Howell Co.

FIG. 77

CHECK PAWL SUPER SPEED MOVEMENT. NO. 1, DRIVING FINGER.

spent in completing the same cycle by the mechanism working at a speed of 128 pictures per second.

The fact that the super-speed mechanisms had proven their worth prior to the advent of talking pictures and had been developed to a high degree of efficiency, and that the speed exigencies for sound work were considerably reduced, mechanical engineers were in a position to carry their investigation mainly upon the silencing of the mechanism, which was brought about by the elimination of all clicking noises produced by ball

Courtesy Bell & Howell Co.

FIG. 78

BELL & HOWELL BELT TIGHTENER AND 400 FOOT MAGAZINE.

bearings, the replacement of steel by fibre gears, and in the Bell & Howell mechanism, by the suppression of three out of the four driving fingers, and the setting of the film tension at from 1½ to 2 ounces, instead of at several pounds as it was set in the earlier models of super-speed mechanisms.

In this movement the tension is applied to the edge of the film, so that the emulsion and back sides of the film are free from friction and, therefore, immune from scratching.

The mechanical noises produced by the various parts

Courtesy Bell & Howell Co.

FIG. 79

BELL & HOWELL BELT TIGHTENER AND 1,000 FOOT MAGAZINE. No. 1 SHOWS FABRIC ENDLESS BELT, No. 2, MAGAZINE RUBBER COVER.

and movements of motion picture cameras have forced the operator to inclose his apparatus in especially constructed sound-proof booths, which are still, at this writing, extensively used though they present great inconveniences, the greatest of which are the lack of mobility of the instrument and the necessity of photographing through a glass plate of considerable thickness.

These inconveniences have, of course, the tendency of impairing the photographic quality of the pictures, and considerably reduce the artistic values so essential to any modern motion picture production. It was then necessary to eliminate, or at least reduce the camera noises to such an extent that they would not be "picked-up" by the microphone even if the camera should be set a reasonable nearness to it.

The most audible noises of motion picture cameras were due to the clicking of the spring belt used to rewind the film in the take-up section of the magazine, the clicking noises of the intermittent movement, the elimination of which has been brought forth as described above, the noises peculiar to the enmeshing of the several gears, the clicking noises peculiar to the functioning of the ball bearings whose mission was to render the functioning of the camera even and smooth, and finally, the drumming noises proceeding from the film magazines and due to their shape and hollowness.

Since it would be impossible to describe how these various noises have been eliminated in all the cameras of different manufacture that can be found on the market, we shall briefly mention the measures adopted by the Bell & Howell Company, whose product has received the endorsement of the professional operators throughout the world, and which have been published in a recent issue of the "American Cinematographer."

"The problems involved in the rewinding of the exposed film in the take-up section of the magazine were happily solved from the early days of cinematography by the use of a spring belt sufficiently taut so as to per-

Courtesy Bell & Howell Co.

FIG. 80

FRONT VIEW OF BELL & HOWELL CAMERA EQUIPPED FOR "SOUND WORK" WITH TURRETT AND PLATE REMOVED. NO. 1, FELT LINING OF THE CAMERA SHUTTER. NO. 2, FORMICA (FIBRE) GEAR. NO. 5, ENDLESS BELT. NO. 6, BELT TIGHTENER.

mit an easy winding of the film and sufficiently loose to avoid an excessive tension and to compensate for the reduction in speed of the driving axle of the magazine with the increase in size of the roll of film. The belt was effectively performing its work by skipping and sliding over the magazine pulley whenever the tension was becoming too great.

"The noises produced by the action of the belt, as well as those produced by the belt joint every time it hit or left the magazine pulley, were to be completely eliminated, and after much study and experimentation, an endless fabric belt was adopted, together with a new belt-tightner arrangement which automatically secures the proper tension and uniform take-up of the exposed film regardless of the size of the roll that is being wound.

"This tightner arrangement is provided with special bearings which entirely eliminate any possibility of noise and also present the useful feature that it permits the use of either the 1,000 or the 400 feet magazine at will.

"The careful investigation conducted in order to ascertain the cause of undesirable noises brought forth the fact that the film magazines themselves were producing a drumming effect due to their shape and hollowness.

"The back and cover of the 1,000 foot magazine are therefore drilled with numerous holes, which are so located that they interrupt the sound waves and thus reduce the above mentioned drumming noises. To further insure their complete elimination, the magazines are covered with a thick layer of spongy rubber and have been equipped with especially designed rubbers and hubs which are made with painstaking care and ac-

curacy and which are absolutely free from the noises
previously inherent to these units.

"All other parts of the camera have been subjected
to the same precise investigation and steel gears have
been replaced by formica (fibre) gears whenever neces-

Courtesy Bell & Howell Co.

FIG. 81

CAMERA SHOWING SUPER SPEED MOVEMENT. NO. 3, CHECK
PAWL SUPER SPEED MOVEMENT. NO. 4, FELT LINING OF
CAMERA DOOR.

sary. Ball bearings have been replaced with solid bronze bearings and all clearances and tolerances have been reduced to the minimum, thus eliminating any slight loss in motion and disposing of other sources of noises.

"These last changes have reduced the ease with which the standard camera was operating with almost no effort at all. This difference has nevertheless no influence whatever on the good functioning of the apparatus and does not cause any complication in operating it since all cameras used for sound work are of necessity motor driven.

"The solid bronze bearings have been designed and are made with the utmost care so as to insure their proper functioning and do not require any more than the normal care which is demanded by any precision apparatus.

"To further insure the complete suppression and dampening of any residual noises, the interior of the cameras, as well as the shutter blades, are being dampened by lining them with a sound absorbing felt.

"Through these and other minor changes, it has been possible for the engineers of the Bell & Howell Company to evolve a camera eminently suitable for work on sound pictures, since actual practice on sound stages has proven that no camera extraneous noises were "picked-up" by the microphone when the camera was placed as close as from eight to ten feet from the subject to be photographed and without the protection of the justly maligned and cordially detested camera booth."

This brief authoritative description of the means resorted to in order to silence the motion picture camera to be used for sound work, offers a true conception of the extreme care with which extraneous noises must be eliminated on the talking picture stage.

The sensitiveness of the microphone is extreme and the effect produced upon the audience in a talking picture auditorium by even scarcely audible grating and hissing noises is much more undesirable than the same noises heard, for example, through the loud speaker of any radio receiving set.

The attention of a motion picture audience is so

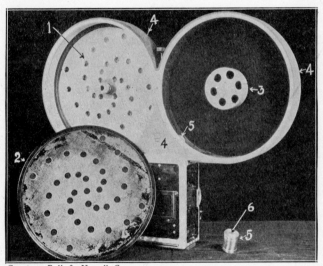

Courtesy Bell & Howell Co.

FIG. 82

BELL & HOWELL 1,000 FOOT MAGAZINES ADAPTED FOR "SOUND WORK." NO. 1, HOLES DRILLED IN BACK OF MAGAZINE. NO. 2, MAGAZINE COVER WITHOUT RUBBER COVER. NO. 3, THREE INCH SPOOL. NO. 4, RUBBER OUTER COVER. NO. 5, FILM ROLLER. NO. 6, OILLESS BEARING OF FILM ROLLER.

keenly attracted by the screen action that the least imperfection in synchronization or the least unnatural noise, the source of which cannot be readily located, becomes so irritating that it is sufficient to completely mar the success of the theatrical presentation of talking pictures.

But a discussion of these considerations is of more interest to the psychologist than to the mechanical engineer, and, therefore, we shall not delve into it in this chapter.

We shall, nevertheless, mention that these psychological or other considerations have provoked the solution of some extremely interesting mechanical problems without the necessity of redesigning new cameras and has brought forth the relatively easy alteration of the standard equipment in use, with no loss whatever in its sturdiness and efficiency.

SOUND RECORDING WITH THE LIGHT VALVE

Speaking at the Fall Convention of the Society of Motion Picture Engineers, Mr. Donald MacKenzie of the Bell Telephone Research Laboratories says: Of the several ways by which sound can be recorded on motion picture film, one has seemed to engineers of Bell Telephone Laboratories to offer most immediate promise. This employs a light beam of constant intensity and varying width to produce a trace of varying density. Modulation of the light beam is effected by an electro-mechanical light valve actuated by speech currents which have been amplified to a suitable volume.

The light valve consists of a loop of duralumin tape suspended in a plane at right angles to a magnetic field. When the assembly of magnet and armature is complete, the two sides of the loop constitute a slit 0.002 by 0.256 inches, its sides lying in a plane at right angles to the lines of force and approximately centred in the air gap. The ends of the loop are connected to the output terminals of the recording amplifier. If the magnet is energized and the amplifier supplies an alternating current, the loop opens and closes in accordance with the current alternations.

When one side of the wave opens the valve to 0.004 inches and the other side closes it completely, full modulation of the aperture is accomplished. The natural frequency of the valve is set by adjusting the tension of the tape; for reasons which involve many considerations, the valve is turned to seven thousand cycles per

second. Under these circumstances about ten milliwatts are required for full modulation at a frequency
remote from resonance; about one one-hundredth of
this power at the resonant frequency. The impedance
of the valve with protecting fuse is about twelve ohms.

If this appliance is interposed between a light source
and a photographic film we have a camera shutter of
unconventional design. Figure 83 shows a diagram of
the optical system for studio recording. At the left is
a light source, a ribbon-filament projection lamp, which
is focused on the plane of the valve. The light passed
by the valve is then focused with a two-to-one reduction on the photographic film at the right. A simple
achromat is used to form the image of the filament at
the valve plane, but a more complicated lens, designed
to exacting specifications by Bausch and Lomb, is required for focusing the valve on the film. The undis-
turbed valve opening appears on the film as a line 0.001
by 0.128 inch, its length at right angles to the direction
of film travel. The width of this line varies with the
sound currents supplied to the valve, so that the film
receives exposure to light of fixed intensity during the
varying time required for a given point to traverse the
varying aperture of the slit.

Recording in the studio is carried out on a film separate from that which receives the picture. This practice permits the use of two machines to make duplicate
sound records, an insurance which is well worth its
cost. The practice of separate negatives for sound and
picture also permits the picture negative to be developed
and printed according to well-established technique, and
allows the necessary latitude in developing the sound
record. The recording machine is driven by a motor
synchronously with the camera. Lest there be any

variation in the velocity of the film past the line of exposure, the sprocket which carries the film at that point is driven through a mechanical filter which holds the instantaneous velocity constant to one part in one thousand.

In the recording machine a photo-electric cell is mounted inside the left hand sprocket which carries the film past the line of exposure. Fresh film transmits some four per cent of the light falling on it, and modulation of this light during the record is appreciated by the cell inside the sprocket. This cell is connected to a preliminary amplifier mounted below the exposure chamber, and with suitable further amplification the operator may hear from the loud speaker the record as it is actually being made on the film. Full modulation of the valve implies complete closing of the slit by one side of the wave of current; this modulation may not be exceeded or photographic overload will abound.

Adding sound to the picture introduces no complication of studio technique other than to require sufficient rehearsing to make sure of satisfactory pick-up of the sound; microphone placement must be established and amplifiers adjusted to feed to the light valve currents which just drive to the edge of overload in the fortissimo passages of music or the loudest utterances of speakers. Provision is made for combining if desired the contributions of several microphones on the set. This combination is under the control of the mixer operator in the monitoring room, who views the set through a double window in the studio wall. The mixer controls also the gain of the amplifiers for the recording machines. Relays permit the mixer to connect the horn circuit either directly to the recording amplifier or to one or the other of the monitoring photo-electric cells in the film recorders. The direct connection is used in preparing the sound pick-up in the studio: the program is rehearsed until satisfactory arrangement of microphones and of amplifier gain is effected. The electrical characteristic of this direct monitoring circuit is so designed that the sound quality heard in the horns shall be the same as the quality to be expected in the reproduction of the positive print in the theatre. Acoustic treatment of the walls of the monitoring room secures the reverberation characteristic of the theatre, and the monitoring level is so adjusted that the mixer operator hears the same loudness that he would wish to hear from the theatre horns. It is capitally important that

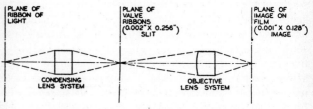

FIG. 83

the operator judge his pick-up on the basis of sound closely identical in loudness and quality with that to be heard later in theatre reproduction.

After the pick-up has been established on the direct monitoring circuit, the output of the recording amplifier is applied to the light valves and the monitoring horns are connected to the photo-electric cell amplifiers on the recording machines. With no film in the machine and at a convenient lamp current a complete rehearsal is made to verify the operation of the valves at the proper level.   Film is then loaded, cameras and sound recorders are interlocked and starting marks made on all films by punches or light flashes.

A light signal from the recording room warns the studio, which after lighting up signals back its readiness to start.   The machine operator starts the cameras and sound recorders, brings up the lamp current to the proper value, and when the machines are up to speed signals the studio to start.   During the recording, the mixer operator monitors the record through the light valves, thereby assuring himself that no record is lost.

In printing these sound negatives in combination with pictures for projection in the theatre, it is customary at the present time to print one negative, masking the space needed for the other, then to run the positive again through the printer with the other negative, masking the space already printed.   In printing the sound negative, the light is regulated to result in thirty-five per cent transmission of the unmodulated track after positive development.   Provision of suitable masks in the camera has been made to show in the finder and expose on the film only the portion which will be available for picture projection.   In the theatre projector, the sound gate is located fourteen and one-half inches below the picture gate, in order to project the sound record at a point where the film is in continuous motion.

As with other systems for sound-transmission, that which includes film recording and reproduction has certain inherent faults which may be minimized by careful design.   These are background noise, irregular response at various frequencies, and distortion due to non-linear characteristics.

Background noise results principally from casual

variations in the light-transmission of both positive and negative films. Raw stock that is entirely satisfactory for pictures may be too irregular for sound records, since the photo-electric cell recognizes variations of 0.1 per cent while the eye ignores contrasts under two per cent. The remedy is to use "positive" stock for the sound negative as well as for the print and to use developer as little granular as possible in its effect. Fortunately, it is necessary to reduce the background noise only to a point below the threshold of audibility which will exist in the theatre during the softer parts of the program. This point determines the level of the faintest sound-record which can be reproduced unmarred by noise.

Due to the facts that the element of illumination is 0.001 inch wide, instead of infinitely narrow, and that the film is traveling at ninety feet per minute, at a frequency of 18,000 cycles per second it will require the time of one cycle of a sound wave for a given point on the film to cross the slit. Then as each successive element of film crosses the slit, it will receive an exposure proportional to the integral of a complete cycle of the valve. Since the integral of one cycle is the same regardless of the phase at which the integral starts, each successive element will receive the same exposure, and the film will develop to a uniform density. Consequently no record will be made of the sound. Fortunately this frequency is far outside the range of interest to us, and the effect decreases as frequencies become lower. The drooping characteristic resulting, called the film transfer loss, may be largely offset by judicious choice of electrical characteristics and by tuning the light-valve mechanically to a frequency near 7,000 cycles.

When the curve connecting power input to the film system with its power output is not a straight line, distortion results, as in purely electrical systems. This takes the form of an introduction of harmonics of the frequencies normally present. The curve which connects exposure of photographic emulsions with resulting opacity is a straight line only when development is so controlled as to produce a contrast-ratio of unity. Picture-recording practice is to develop the positive print to a contrast-ratio greater than unity. Development of the sound-negative is therefore so controlled as to give a contrast-ratio the reciprocal of that to be expected in the positive, so that the overall ratio is unity. Distortion from this cause is then so completely annulled that the resulting harmonics are undetectible.

The correction just outlined is available over only that part of the photographic range where exposure is correct. For exposures outside this range, the characteristic curve of film becomes curved in a way which cannot be compensated in the printing, and a liberal crop of harmonics is inevitable. However, the range of positive film is about twenty to one, and with the combination of light-source and optical system developed in Bell Telephone Laboratories, it is not difficult to set the unmodulated light at a value which will give an exposure of ten times that corresponding to the beginning of under-exposure. Then ninety per cent modulation of the light can be permitted without running into exposure on the "faint" side of the wave. For sound currents reaching one hundred per cent modulation of the light, ninety per cent of the wave is free from distortion; if the average light were halved, still eighty per cent would be free from distortion. There is therefore considerable latitude in the average exposure, and the negative is satisfactory if the transmission of the unmodulated track lies between fairly wide limits.

The volume of reproduced sound for a given reproducing light source varies directly with the average track density and the per cent modulation of this average. In printing the sound negative, a uniform density for the print of the unmodulated track is desired, lest there be changes in the sound output during the showing. For Eastman positive film a suitable transmission of the unmodulated portion of the sound print is thirty-five per cent. At this average transmission only the peaks of the recorded sound will encroach on the region of under-exposure. For the reciprocally-developed negative track the region of under-exposure will have been reached by occasional peaks on the other side of the wave, and whatever photographic distortion exists will be balanced between positive and negative.

If the entire negative exposure has been confined to the under-exposure region of the emulsion chosen, a huskiness in the reproduction will result which can not be corrected by any known technique. But with correct exposure, which is readily possible with the light-valve method, ninety per cent of the wave will be clear of under-exposure, and experience shows that the ear detects no distortion. In telephonic terms, everything at a level one TU below full modulation will be free from distortion, and the peaks will be substantially perfect.

RCA PHOTOPHONE

RCA PHOTOPHONE employs two methods of recording and reproducing sound. In the first process a sound track is printed adjacent to the picture frames of the Motion Picture film. The advantage of this system is obvious in that synchronism between picture and sound is automatically maintained.

In addition to the sound track method of recording and reproducing, RCA Photophone manufactures disc recorders and reproducers. The sound is recorded upon a record somewhat similar to a phonograph disc. Reproduction is accomplished by the use of a needle and a magnetic pick-up.

The Photophone projector is equipped in such a manner that either sound film or disc may be used. Both processes and the equipment employed are described in the following pages.

Recording. Sound Motion Pictures recorded and reproduced by the film method may be briefly described by assuming that we have a series of transformations with the film as the centre of these transformations. The film has on it both the picture and sound track. The transformations which are made in connection with Sound Motion Pictures on film consist of changing sound waves into electrical waves, the electrical waves into light waves, recording these light waves on film, converting back to light waves, then to electrical waves, and finally into audible sound waves. In effect, the film provides a means for taking sound waves and storing them for any period of time. In the beginning, there is the sound which is to be recorded. These

FIG. 84

RCA PROJECTOR.

sound waves are picked up by means of a condenser microphone similar to that used in radio broadcasting stations. The microphone converts the sound into electrical waves. A suitable amplifying system increases the level of these waves and in turn operates an oscillograph element or vibrator. This element has a mirror which reflects a beam of light onto the moving film where the vibrations are recorded. This film is properly developed and any desired number of prints made from it. Any one of these films may then serve to reproduce the original sound. In the Reproducing System the film is drawn past a constant source of light and the variations on the film change the amount of light entering a sensitive cell. These light waves are translated into electrical waves by this photo-electric cell and the electrical waves are amplified by a suitable system. The power from the amplifying system is led to the loud-speakers where it is changed into sound waves. The sounds reproduced by the loud-speaker system will correspond to those which were picked up by the microphone in the Recording System.

The second method by which Synchronized Motion Pictures are made is that in which the sound is recorded on a wax disc and reproduced by a system which corresponds to the electrical phonograph. With this system there are the same number of transformations, but the storing medium is different. As in the case of film recording, the sounds are picked up by a microphone which changes the sound waves into electrical waves. These electrical waves are amplified by a suitable system, the output of which is connected to the recording device. In this case the vibrator and light source are replaced by a record cutter. The sound is recorded on a wax disc which rotates at constant speed while being drawn under the record cutter. The resulting spiral groove contains the sound record. Any desired number of records may be made from this original master wax; thus, this wax and the corresponding records serve the same purpose with this system as do the films in the previous system. For reproduction from disc the record is driven at constant speed and a magnetic pick-up translates the variations in the record into electrical energy. When amplified by a suitable system the original sounds are reproduced by the loud-speaker system. As in the case of film recording, the reproduced sounds will correspond to the sounds which were originally picked up by the microphone.

There are two general types of Sound Motion Pictures. One of these is synchronized after the Motion Picture itself has been completed and is simply a silent film made into a sound picture. The other is recorded simultaneously with the taking of the picture itself. The former will of course contain only music and effects and will have no talking sequences, while in the latter the characters may actually talk.

The methods used in producing the two types of pictures are entirely different and will be briefly described. For the first, which is simply a sound picture, the complete Motion Picture is taken and the music or sound effects added later. The picture is shown and the musical score arranged, then the actual synchronization is begun. As a rule, the picture is projected on a screen just as in a theatre. The orchestra accompanies the picture with the musical score as previously arranged. At the same time the recording equipment is put in operation and the musical score recorded. The sound film is then developed and printed on the same film with the picture. Special precautions must be taken so that the complete sound picture will have the musical score properly synchronized. This is brought about by having the projector and the recorder both

Courtesy RCA Photophone

FIG. 85

RCA CAMERA FOR SOUND AND PICTURE RECORDING.

driven by synchronous motors so that the film runs through both machines at exactly the same rate of speed. The same amount of film will then be run through each of the two machines and resulting print will be properly synchronized. In the actual printing, the sound is placed ahead of the corresponding action by a distance of approximately 19 frames. This is done so that the film may pass through the projector mechanism which contains the intermittent movement and be drawn through the sound head mechanism at absolutely constant speed.

In the second type of synchronized picture the method of recording is entirely different. In this case both the action and the sounds are recorded simultaneously. The action will be photographed in the usual way with the exception that there must be absolute quiet and the camera must be motor driven. At the same time that the picture is being recorded, the sound recording machine, which is usually located in a room adjacent to the stage itself, records the sound. This recorder is likewise motor driven and the camera and recorder are so arranged that the same amount of film is run through each. Both the camera and the recording machine are controlled from a common point so that the two start simultaneously. In order that the sound and action may be properly synchronized, a system of marking is used. This marker simply leaves a visible mark on each film so that when the two are developed they may be printed together on one film in the proper relation. As in the previous case, the sound is placed ahead of the corresponding action by a distance of approximately 19 frames. Pictures of this latter type are generally recorded in sound proof studios, excepting of course, the well known News Reels, and the utmost precautions are used to prevent the recording of undesirable sounds. Special cameras which are practically noiseless have been developed for this type of work, and in some cases the cameras are placed inside sound proof booths.

The methods of synchronizing the sound-on-film will also apply largely to the sound-on-disc principle of recording. As in the former, the synchronized record may contain simply the musical score with effects, or it may contain actual talking sequences. The disc recording equipment is driven by a synchronous motor in the same fashion as the film recorder which has just been described. RCA Photophone utilizes both methods of recording and the reproducing equipment is installed so that either type of recording may be reproduced.

There are two general methods used for recording sound-on-film. One of these is known as the Variable Density Method and the other as the Variable Area Method. In the former the sound track on the film appears as a narrow strip with lines of varying darkness passing across it. In the latter the sound track appears as a jagged edge with half the area dark and the other half light. With this system of recording the sound wave is actually placed on the film and can be seen in much the same way as one sees the recorded sounds on an ordinary phonograph record. The Variable Area Method has the advantage that film development and exposure are not as critical as in the former method. Since the reproduction of the sound depends entirely upon the amount of light which strikes the photo-electric cell, either type of film may be used in the same apparatus.

The Recording System employed by RCA Photophone consists of three essential parts; first, the microphone which picks up the sound wave; second, a vacuum tube amplifying system; third, a recorder for putting the sound waves on the film. The microphone which is

Courtesy RCA Photophone

FIG. 86

AMPLIFYING PANELS FOR TYPE "A" INSTALLATION.

used is of the condenser type and has been choosen because of its reliability and extreme quietness in operation. The number of microphones used for any given
recording depends upon the conditions. Where a single speaker is to be recorded, only one microphone is

Courtesy RCA Photophone

FIG. 87

RCA PHOTOPHONE MOTOR GENERATOR EQUIPMENT FOR TYPE
"A" INSTALLATIONS.

likely to be used, whereas for a symphony orchestra as
many as three or more microphones are likely to be
employed. An amplifier takes the minute electrical
variations from the microphone and amplifies them to
any desired level. This amplifier is made with a gain
control which determines the output volume and it is

also equipped with a mixer panel with which the signal from any desired microphone can be controlled and kept at the proper level with respect to the other microphones. From the amplifier the signal is led to the recorder, which is usually located in the same room.

The RCA Photophone Recorder is a device which changes the electrical signal from the amplifier into light waves, and in turn impresses these waves upon the film. The signal from the amplifier causes the oscillograph element to vibrate and reflect a beam of light through a suitable optical system onto the moving film. The film is drawn past the light slit at a constant speed of ninety feet per minute. It will be seen that any variations in film speed due to changing motor speed or back lash in gears will cause objectionable ripples or "wow-wows" in the completed film. For this reason it is necessary to keep absolutely constant and uniform film speed past the light slit.

In the same room with the Photophone Recorder and associated amplifying system there is a monitoring loud-speaker by means of which the recording engineer is able to hear exactly what is being recorded on the film. This loud-speaker is especially useful when making tests in the studio, before actual production is begun. It is generally assumed that the monitoring loud-speaker is used by the recording engineer in controlling the output volume of the amplifying system, but this is not necessarily true. While the monitoring loud-speaker might be used for such a purpose, other more accurate means are available. One of these consists of an output meter or modulation meter, which is included in the amplifying equipment and shows the true output of the system. The other method is that of actually watching the light beam which is being recorded upon the film.

Sounds are recorded on Photophone film on a sound track 70 mils in width and the amplitude of the recorded waves must be such that all sounds are recorded within this 70 mil width. As a rule the recording engineer will place a card in a portion of the light beam where it will not interfere with the light falling on the film. With this system it is possible actually to see the volume of sound which is being recorded on the film as well as to hear it on the monitoring loud-speaker.

The method of recording sound on disc records for talking Motion Pictures is much the same as that employed for commercial phonograph records. The sound pick-up and amplifying systems are practically the same as used for the film recorder. The sound is recorded on a soft wax disc and from this disc the finished records are made. In the actual recording, the wax disc is placed upon a large turntable which is driven at absolutely constant speed by means of a synchronous motor. As the disc rotates the sounds are recorded on the wax by use of a device known as the record cutter. This cutter is connected to the amplifier in practically the same way as is the oscillograph used in the film recorder. The cutter is made with a sharp cutting material such as sapphire. At the same time that the disc is rotating, it is moved sideways at a uniform speed so that the resulting record consists of a spiral groove. The finished record looks like the standard phonograph record with the exception that it is considerably larger. In spite of this resemblance, there are two major differences. First, the disc which is recorded for synchronous reproduction runs at a speed of 33 1/3 revolutions per minute instead of the usual 78 revolutions per minute specified for the standard phonograph, and second, in starting the record which is recorded for synchronous reproduction, the magnetic pick-up is placed at the centre of the record and travels outward towards the outer edge, the reverse of the procedure with stand-

Courtesy RCA Photophone

FIG. 88

RCA INPUT CONTROL PANEL. LOCATED IN PROJECTION ROOM. (TYPE "C" INSTALLATIONS.)

ard phonograph records. The record cutter is somewhat similar in appearance to the well known magnetic pick-up used in connection with electrical reproduction of standard phonograph records, but in this case the action is reversed. The electrical energy from the amplifying system actuates the cutter armature and causes the cutting point to vibrate in accordance with the sound vibrations which strike the microphone pick-up.

Reproducing. Any system which reproduces sound from film may be divided into three general classifications. First, the pick-up device; second, the amplifying device; third, the loudspeaker. It is evident that fundamentally all systems for reproducing sound from film are similar. There is a lamp, and the light from this lamp passes through the film onto a light sensitive cell. The output from this cell is amplified and fed into the loud-speakers. In the matter of connecting the light sensitive cell to the amplifier, the RCA Photophone system of sound reproducing equipment differs from others.

It had been assumed that owing to the inherent characteristics of the light cell it was necessary to locate the first amplifier alongside this cell or very near it. This meant that a portion of the amplifying equipment had to be mounted on the projector itself. It was found that by using a suitable photo-electric cell and specially designed transformers it was possible to locate the amplifier at some distance from the photo-cell itself. This difference has meant a reduction in the amount of equipment attached to, or located adjacent to, each projector. With this system all that is necessary as part of the regular projection equipment is some device which will cause the film to be drawn through the sound equipment at absolutely constant speed, and a lamp to be used as a photo-cell exciter lamp, the photo-cell itself, and the photo-cell transformer. All of the amplifying equipment is then located in one unit, usually in the back of the projection room, where there is more space available and the equipment is more accessible.

One other point also influenced the engineers of RCA Photophone and its associated companies in the development of this system. It is well known that the ordinary vacuum tube is quite sensitive to mechanical vibration as well as to electrical signals. If the tube in an amplifying system is struck even a light blow, an unpleasant thump will be heard in the loud-speakers. It the tube is placed where it is constantly vibrating, these vibrations may be heard in the loud-speakers. Thus, if a portion of the amplifier is located on the projector proper, there is some possibility of the vibrations being transmitted to the loud-speakers so that they will be heard in the theatre. With the RCA Photophone method of pick-up, these objectionable features are eliminated.

For high quality reproduction, every element in the reproducing system as well as in the recording system must be as nearly perfect as possible. The various units going to make up Photophone recording and reproducing apparatus approach this perfection more nearly than was thought possible a very short time ago. It is well known that high quality sound reproduction should contain all frequencies from about 60 cycles to at least 6,000 cycles. The amplifying equipment used by RCA Photophone has been designed with this end in view and the amplifiers have been made to reproduce all frequencies from below 60 cycles to well above 6,000 cycles, in practically equal amounts. With such a range as this it is possible to reproduce recorded sounds or music with a high degree of fidelity.

In addition to good amplifying equipment it is evident that the loud-speaker equipment employed for sound reproduction must be of very high quality if the projected sound is to be comparable to the original. RCA Photophone employs moving coil loud-speakers of the cone type throughout. Each loud-speaker cone is 12 inches in diameter and the number of loud-speakers depends upon the type of amplifying equipment which is installed. In each case the loud-speakers are distributed on the sides and above the screen and are directed into the auditorium in such a way that practically perfect sound distribution is secured, along with the illusion that the sound is originating in the screen itself. The loud-speakers are fitted with heavy wood baffle boards which aid materially in the reproduction of low frequencies. With this type of loud-speaker and baffle all frequencies are reproduced, so that every instrument from the bass drum to frequencies well above the highest notes of the piccolo, are reproduced.

RCA PHOTOPHONE PROJECTOR

THE RCA Photophone Projector was designed to meet the exacting requirements of modern Motion Picture projection with synchronized sound effects.

The projector is a combination picture and sound reproducer, the projection and the soundheads being confined to a single housing. The machine is designed in such a manner that it is adaptable to all existing types of synchronized sound film. A distinct advantage of the RCA Photophone Projector is manifest in the location of the film shutter, the light being cut before entering the projector head. This arrangement reduces the heat on the film by 60%, and, as can be readily realized, greatly lessens the tendency of the film to buckle. The result is a clearer and more sharply defined image on the picture screen, and likewise a marked decrease in fire hazard.

The gearing of the projector is lubricated by means of a unique and highly efficient forced feed oil system. The oil tank is affixed to the lower front wall of the projection head casting. An oil pump within the projection head serves to distribute and maintain in circulation the correct quantity of the lubricating medium.

The principle upon which the RCA Photophone projector operates is as follows:

The sound film, having passed through the picture projector, enters the sound reproducing chamber. This statement is made merely to show the path of the film because it is obvious that the sound record must pass through the sound reproducing mechanism at the exact instant that its corresponding picture is passing through the film gate.   To accomplish this, the sound record is printed on the film 19 frames in advance of the picture.

A graphic reproduction of the sound wave is printed upon the side of the Motion Picture film.   This sound track, as it is called, passes before a beam of light pro-

Courtesy RCA Photophone

FIG. 89

RCA Photophone P.2. Projector with Sound Film Pick-Up.

jected upon it from an exciter lamp optical system. The light passes through the film in direct proportion to the variations of the sound wave, then enters the window or cleared section of a photo-electric cell. The impedance of the cell varies with the increase and the decrease of the amount of light passing through the film. These variations correspond to the frequency and amplitude of the sound wave recorded upon the film.

The photo-electric cell mentioned in the foregoing paragraph is an unique light sensitive device which owes its origin to Elster and Geitel, who, while experimenting with the electropositive metals, sodium, potassium, and rubidium, demonstrated that these metals manifest photo-electric effects. The changing intensity of the light caused by the variations of clear and dark areas in the sound track, as has been stated, produces a simultaneous change in the impedance of the photo-electric cell, which in turn causes a corresponding change in the current through the cell. The output terminals of the photo-electric cell are connected to the input terminals of an audio frequency amplifier. Here the signal is stepped up to the required volume and the output coupled to the loud-speakers, which are located in close proximity to the Motion Picture screen.

It has been stated that recording is done at constant sprocket hole speed. When the RCA Photophone projector is examined it will be found that this machine also contains a compensator and likewise has the film running over a drum. It would appear that the action in the recorder and in the projector are the same, but this is not the case. In the projector the sound drum is driven at absolutely constant speed by means of a synchronous motor drive, or constant speed direct current motor drive, and the drum is attached to a fly wheel. The compensator functions similar to that in the recorder, but in this case the speed of the driving sprockets is varied. In this way the sound is reproduced at absolutely constant linear film speed.

Courtesy RCA Photophone

FIG. 90

PROJECTOR WITH RCA PHOTOPHONE FILM AND DISC "PICK-UP" ATTACHMENT.

The compensator itself is controlled by the movement of an arm carrying an idler roller over which the film runs. Upon threading up, this arm is left in about the middle position of its swing and is held there by the film. This compensator arm is immediately ahead of the sound drum. After passing over the sound drum the film runs over a take-up idler. This idler has a spring tension to take up slack and to keep the film tight on the sound drum.

The action of the compensator in the Photophone projector is as follows:

Assume that the projector has been threaded with the compensator arm in the mid position and that the take-up idler is likewise in a position near the middle of its swing. Assuming that the film has been properly threaded through the projector mechanism and over the various sprockets, the projector is now ready for operation. Let us first suppose that the film which is being used has not been shrunk. In this case the sprocket hole speed and the linear speed of the film will be exactly the same, so that the film will pass around the drum as fast as it is fed from the sprockets, thus keeping the compensator arm and the take-up idler in exactly the same position as they were upon starting. Should this supposedly perfect film continue to pass through the projector, this same condition will remain. In actual operation such a uniform film is never encountered, and it is for exactly this reason that the compensator has been included in the Photophone projector. Let us assume that the film is passing through the projector, as stated before. Now suppose that a piece of film is encountered which has been shrunk, so that while the number of sprocket holes per minute may remain constant, the actual footage of film will be slightly decreased. This condition would mean that the film would be torn. Before this point is reached, the Photophone compensator comes into use and prevents it. As the footage of film is decreased, the loop ahead of the sound drum becomes smaller and pulls down the compensator arm. As soon as this arm is pulled down a brake inside the projector mechanism brings into play a set of gears somewhat similar to the transmission gears of a model "T" Ford automobile, which act to speed up all the sprockets in the projector. The speed of the sound drum remains constant, hence the loop ahead of the sound drum immediately becomes larger. As soon as this loop is large enough, the compensator brake disengages and the sprocket speed and drum speed are again the same.

For the reproduction of music, etc., which has been recorded on synchronous discs, a synchronous disc attachment is provided with the RCA Photophone projector. This attachment is fastened to the "A" frame of the projector in such a manner that the projector head may be tilted to any projection angle while the disc turntable remains in a level position. The turntable is entirely supported by the projector frame and is actually a component part of the projector. It is driven by the projector motor by means of a flexible coupling, thus securing absolute synchronism between the projector and the disc. A specially designed magnetic pick-up forms part of the turntable equipment and insures accurate sound reproduction. The output of the magnetic pick-up is coupled to the input of the standard Photophone amplifying equipment through a switching arrangement which enables the operator to transfer from the disc pick-up to the film pick-up.

RCA Photophone Sound Attachment. In addition
to the Photophone projector RCA Photophone manufactures a sound attachment which is used in conjunction with certain types of commercial projectors and
contains the necessary mechanism for running sound
films. The sound attachment is suspended directly below the projection head and comprises an exciter lamp
system, an optical system, a sound head, a photo-electric cell with transformer, and the requisite gearing for
driving the film through the sound head at constant
speed. As has been previously stated, it is necessary
in running pictures which have the sounds recorded on
film that the film be drawn through the sound mechanism at a uniform speed. The Photophone Sound Attachment employs a mechanical filtering system to sta-
bilize the movement of the film and prevent undesirable
jerking and vibration such as might be occasioned by
back lash in gears. There is a uniform speed sprocket
which pulls the film through the sound gate. This
sprocket has attached to it a fly wheel which prevents
instantaneous changes in speed. Even this fly wheel
would be insufficient however, if it were not for the
flexible coupling between the uniform speed sprocket
and the remainder of the mechanism. This sprocket is
driven through a spring coupling so that any jerking
in the projector mechanism will not be transmitted to
the uniform speed sprocket. There is also a damping
device which aids in stabilizing this drive. The damping action is secured by having a constant pressure
exerted on the fly wheel through a leather washer which
runs in petroleum jelly. The resultant damping action
is controlled by means of an adjustment on the sound
attachment and this adjustment is made so that the uni-

form speed sprocket drives the film through the sound attachment at absolutely uniform speed.

The principle involved in the reproduction of sound is the same as that described in the paragraphs devoted to this subject in connection with the RCA Photophone projector. The light from the exciter lamp passes through the film and on to the photo-electric cell. This cell is coupled to the Photophone amplifier by means of the photo-cell transformer previously described. Each attachment is equipped with three exciter lamps and these lamps are pre-focused so that in case one lamp burns out, another may be substituted for it simply by turning a handle which is located beneath the lamp housing. The time required for this substitution is a matter of seconds, which means that the sound will not be held up during a show because of a burned-out exciter lamp.

In addition to the sound attachment, which is used for reproducing sound on film, RCA Photophone manufactures a synchronous disc attachment for standard projectors so that synchronous disc records may be reproduced. This synchronous disc stands on a pedestal which is separate from the projector itself and is protected by a substantial guard rail. The turntable is driven by the projector motor through a flexible coupling. In order to prevent undesirable variations in the instantaneous speed of the disc, the attachment is fitted with a mechanical filter system consisting of a vane which floats in oil. As a result of this construction the disc rotates at absolutely uniform speed and the reproduced sounds are free from objectionable changes in pitch, commonly known at "wow-wows."

A magnetic pick-up similar to that used on the RCA Photophone projector is employed to pick up the sounds from the disc. This pick-up is connected to the amplifier in such a way that by throwing a single switch the input from the amplifier may be transferred from film

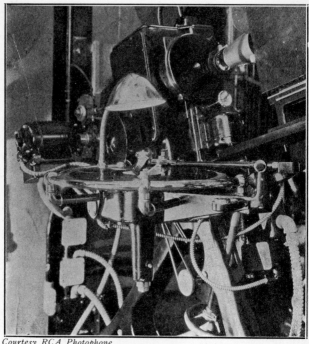

Courtesy RCA Photophone

FIG. 91

PHOTOPHONE DISC TURNTABLE.

to disc. The film-disc transfer switch is located on the front wall of the projection room directly in front of the projectionist. This transfer switch also contains the disc volume control which may be used in addition to the regular volume control on the RCA Photophone amplifier.

Amplifiers. RCA Photophone manufactures five types of amplifying equipment for the theatre installation. The type of amplifier installed depends upon the size of the house and its acoustic properties. For the largest houses the equipment is known as Type "A," and for the smallest houses as Type "D," with the remaining types for intermediate size houses. There are two types of amplifying equipment known as the "B" equipment and these equipments are distinguished by the letters (MG) and (SPU). These two types of equipments have been designed for the same size houses and differ only in the source of power and for this reason have been given the same type letter.

Amplifiers Types "A" and "B" (MG). RCA Photophone manufactures two types of equipment supplied by power from motor-generator sets. The Type "A" equipment consists of either two RCA Photophone projectors or two standard projection machines equipped with RCA Photophone sound attachments, two amplifier racks, one of which is a spare, two 4-unit motor-generator sets, four storage batteries, twelve RCA Photophone electro-dynamic 12-inch cone type loud-speakers, and all necessary installation and operating accessories. The amplifiers together with the 4-unit motor-generator sets and storage batteries are furnished in duplicate. Only one amplifier is used for regular show operation. The other is kept in readiness as standby equipment, and in case of an emergency may be placed in service in a very short time.

The power supply for the 4-unit motor-generator sets may be either 110 volts DC or 220 volts, three phase alternating current. Each of these MG sets is provided with approved fused line switches, and with automatic starters remote controlled from the amplifier racks.

The Type "B" (MG) equipment consists of two RCA Photophone Projectors or two standard projection machines equipped with RCA Photophone sound attachments. One amplifier rack, one 4-unit motor-generator set, two storage batteries, twelve RCA Photophone electro-dynamic 12 inch cone loud-speakers, and all necessary installation and operating accessories. The amplifier used in this equipment consists of one voltage amplifier and two power amplifiers. Normally the two power amplifiers are used, each amplifier operating 6 of the 12 inch dynamic cone speakers. The power amplifiers are so arranged that in case one fails the show can proceed with one amplifier. The 4-unit motor-generator set used with the Type "B" amplifier is similar to the one used in the Type "A" equipment.

The Types "A" and "B" equipments are similar in construction and operation. The Type "A" equipment has duplicate amplifier racks and affords a complete standby equipment, whereas the Type "B" equipment has one rack with two power amplifiers, and in case of emergency this equipment may be operated with only one of the power amplifiers.

It is to be noted that all power for the "A" and "B" (MG) amplifier is supplied by motor-generator sets, thus eliminating the necessity for batteries. The two storage batteries with each equipment are used as filters to smooth out generator ripple and are not used as a source of power.

Amplifiers Types "B" (SPU), "C" and "D." RCA Photophone manufactures three types of amplifiers which are operated from a regular 110 volt, alternating current lighting circuit. The smallest of these is known as Type "D" and is installed in houses with a seating capacity of 750 or less. With this type equipment two RCA Photophone projectors or two standard projectors with Photophone Sound Attachments are installed. The same applies to the Type "C" equipment which is used for houses seating up to 1,500, and the Type "B" (SPU) for houses larger than 1,500.

With each of these equipments an input control panel is located on the front wall of the projection room. This panel has meters and rheostats for controlling the current in the photo-cell exciter lamps; a change-over potentiometer for changing from one machine to the other; a volume control and a volume indicating meter. Unlike the two equipments previously described, these types have no high voltage lines entering from the outside, but are constructed with rectifying units for supplying plate voltage. The three types are essentially the same, the only difference being in the number of units installed.

The Type "D" equipment has one voltage amplifier unit and one power amplifier unit and operates four 12 inch dynamic cone loud-speakers. The Type "C" equipment has two voltage amplifier units, one of which is not in use but is held as standby equipment, and two power amplifier units, both of which are in use feeding eight dynamic speakers. The Type "B" (SPU) has two voltage amplifier units, one of which is a standby, and four power amplifier units, all of which are used to operate sixteen loud-speakers. In case of trouble with the voltage amplifier unit it is possible to switch to the standby by throwing a series of three switches. This operation takes less than one-half minute. In case of trouble with a power amplifier unit, this particular unit is cut out and the show run on the remaining units.

Each power amplifier and voltage amplifier unit is provided with its own controls and is operated independently of the others. All of these amplifiers use the

Courtesy RCA Photophone

FIG. 92

PHOTOPHONE ATTACHMENT ON SIMPLEX PROJECTOR.

standard RCA Radiotrons, which are widely known for their consistent good service. Filament current for the voltage amplifier units and for the photo-cell exciter lamps is furnished by a storage battery. Each installation has two storage batteries, one for use while the other is being charged. All wiring from the projectors to the amplifiers, and from the amplifiers to the batteries and loud-speakers is pulled in suitable conduit and concealed. For installations where the theatre does not have 110 volt, 60 cycle, alternating current supply available, convertors or transformers for changing to such power are installed. Two convertors are supplied with Types "C" and "B" (SPU) equipment, one to be used as standby equipment. With the Type "D" equipment only one convertor is supplied.

With the equipments outlined above, the following advantages are evident:

1. All controls necessary for running the show, changing projectors and controlling volume are located on the front wall of the projection room, directly in front of the projectionist and easily accessible.

2. Adequate standby equipment is provided in the larger equipments so that the show will go on even in an emergency.

3. All outside power to the amplifiers is furnished by regular 110 volt, 60 cycle, alternating current lighting supply.

4. All high voltage is completely enclosed within the amplifier and the amplifier itself is enclosed in a metal case.

5. The Type "D" installation can be converted into the Type "C" installation in a very short time by the addition of one voltage amplifier unit and one power amplifier unit with proper inter-connecting cables.

RCA TECHNICAL INFORMATION

Type "A" Amplifier. In Type "A" equipment the amplifiers are in duplicate, one being a spare. They are mounted in separate racks placed adjacent to each other. These two amplifiers are identical except that one of them is equipped with a loud-speaker sectionalizing panels.

Starting at the top of the rack, each amplifier comprises the following units:

An input control panel, a voltage amplifier panel, a power amplifier panel, a power control panel and on one of the racks a loud-speaker sectionalizing panel. The latter space on the other amplifier is occupied by a blank panel.

The Input Panel. The input panel has duplicate controls, one set for each projector. The controls for one projector are on the left of the panel. The controls for the other projector are on the right. For each projector, there is on this panel:

A gang switch the function of which is to connect the amplifier to the exciter lamp and photo-cell of that particular projector. An exciter lamp rheostat to regulate the current of the exciter lamp. A pilot lamp to indicate which projector is being used and a jack employed in conjunction with the test meter on the control panel to measure the exciter lamp current.

Voltage Amplifier Panel. After passing through the input panel the signal enters the voltage amplifier and passes through three stages of amplification. The signal from the projector first passes through a transformer similar to that in the projector itself and this transformer applies the signal to the grid of the first tube. This tube is coupled to the second tube by a step-up transformer. The first and third stages use UX-210 Radiotrons and the second stage uses a UX-841 Radiotron. Grid bias voltage is supplied by dry batteries and plate voltage is supplied by a 500-volt tap on the 1,000-volt generator. The plate circuit of each tube is designed with a filter arrangement which prevents objectionable hum from the generator being heard in the loud-speakers. Jacks are provided for reading the plate current of each tube and for reading the bias voltage. The gain control mentioned above regulates the volume to any desired level. At the left of the gain control there is located a jack marked "Phonograph Pick-up" which permits the use of non-synchronous equipment in conjunction with the regular amplifying system.

Power Amplifier Panel. Upon emerging from the voltage amplifier, the signal enters the power amplifier. The power amplifier panel comprises two separate panels, the upper one having a screened opening which allows ventilation for the two rows of tubes mounted behind the lower panel. These consist of ten UV-845 Radiotrons. The amplifier is of the push-pull type.

The lower panel contains two plate current meters, a meter for measuring the speaker current and two rheostat dials for controlling the plate current.

A monitoring loud-speaker to check the sound may be plugged into a jack located to the left of the speaker current meter.

Power Control Panel. On this panel the power controls are mounted. They comprise:

A motor-generator "Start-Stop" switch with an indicating lamp beside it. A tumbler switch (at the lower right of the panel) which applies the voltage to the filaments, grids, and plates of the tubes. Four jacks are provided on the panel. The plate voltages of the power amplifier, the grid voltage of the power amplifier, and the filament voltage of all tubes may be determined by plugging a meter into the respective jacks.

Three meters are mounted in the centre of the panel. An ammeter with a zero centre is on the right and indicates the charge or discharge current in the battery circuit. The other two meters are for testing purposes and are used in conjunction with the jacks on all panels when checking the various circuits.

Loud-speaker Sectionalizing Panel. This panel is located at the bottom of one of the amplifier racks. The other amplifier rack is supplied with a blank panel in this position. On the panel are mounted the output switches which connect the loud-speakers to the amplifiers. There is provision for cutting off each pair of loud-speakers and for cutting off the entire group. There is also provision for transferring the entire group of loud-speakers from one amplifier rack to the other. In case of trouble with the amplifier which is in operation with the motor-generator set the spare amplifier is started, the output signal is switched to the spare amplifier and the input is switched by opening the two gang switches on the regular amplifier and closing the two gang switches on the spare amplifier. This operation takes a very short time so that the independent system may be placed in operation almost before the audience is aware that trouble exists.

Motor Generator Set. All power for operating the Type "A" equipment is supplied by a 4-unit motor-generator set which is usually installed in the regular generator room of the theatre. This unit consists of a 4-horsepower driving motor and the following generators:

A 250-volt generator which supplies field current for the other generators, bias voltage for the power tubes and field current for the loud-speakers.

A 15-volt generator which supplies current for lighting the filament of all tubes, pilot lights and photo-cell exciter lamps.

A 1,000-volt machine which supplies plate current for all tubes and the polarizing voltage for the photo-electric cells. This machine has two commutators so that it also supplies current at 500 volts potential.

Storage Batteries. Each Type "A" amplifier is supplied with a 12-volt storage battery of low capacity. These batteries are floated across the 15-volt generator and are used normally as filters for taking out generator ripple. Only in extreme emergencies are they used as an actual source of power.

Visual Signal System. In order that the volume of sound from the loud-speakers may be kept at the proper level, RCA Photophone installs a visual signal system in the projection room, and this system is controlled by push buttons located at some suitable point in the theatre. Two types of signal stations are supplied. One of these has lamps which are lighted when the button is pressed and thus show the operator what change is desired. A buzzer which is included as a part of the signal station attracts the operator's attention. The second system employs a standard 3-drop annunciator. When a button is pressed, one drop falls and a buzzer attracts the operator's attention. The drop remains down until the operator resets it.

Projection Room Monitor. With each installation RCA Photophone installs a projection room monitor. This is a standard loud-speaker, connected to the output of the amplifier so that the operator may hear what is being reproduced by the auditorium loud-speakers. This monitor is not intended to be used for controlling volume but is useful in determining whether or not the equipment is operating properly, and in testing.

Type "B" Amplifier. In the Type "B" equipment one amplifier rack is used, consisting of the following panels: An input and voltage amplifier panel. Two Power amplifier panels. A power control panel.

Input and Voltage Amplifier Panels. The input and voltage amplifier panel is made as a single unit and is quite similar to the corresponding two panels of the Type "A" amplifier. Duplicate controls on the panel are provided for two projectors. They consist of two exciter lamp rheostats with corresponding meter jacks, two projector control switches with corresponding pilot lamps to indicate which projector is connected to the amplifier, a single test meter with cord extension, and jacks for reading plate current and bias voltage. With one exception the voltage amplifier is similar to the one used in Type "A" amplifier. The Type "B" voltage amplifier has the gain control following the second stage. The first and third stages are UX-210 Radiotrons and the second stage used a UX-841 Radiotron.

Power Amplifier Panels. The two power amplifier panels are similar in construction and operation. Each consists of four UV-845 Radiotrons connected push-pull parallel. On the panel are mounted two plate current meters which indicate the plate current in the front and back row of tubes respectively, two potentiometers for adjusting the bias voltage to obtain the proper plate current reading, a power switch, a monitoring loud-speaker jack and a loud-speaker switch. Each power amplifier operates a bank of six RCA Photophone loud-speakers.

Power Control Panel. The power control panel consists of a motor-generator "Start-Stop" switch with a pilot light to connect when the motor-generator set is in operation, a rheostat to control the generator voltages and jacks appropriately marked for filament, bias and plate voltage readings.

Loudspeaker Sectionalizing Panel. On the side of the amplifier rack is located a small loud-speaker sectionalizing switch panel. Six switches are mounted on this panel and are used for controlling the loud-speakers, in groups of two.

Auxiliary Equipment. The motor-generator set, storage batteries, projection room monitor and visual signal system which are used with Type "B" (MG) amplifier are the same as those used with Type "A" amplifier.

Types "B" (SPU) "C" and "D" Amplifiers. As previously stated, these amplifiers are made up of similar parts and differ only in the number of units in use. The essential parts of each type are the input control panel, the voltage amplifier unit, the power amplifier unit, the battery equipment.

Input Control Panel. The input control panel used in RCA Photophone equipments Type "B" (SPU), "C" and "D" contains a change-over potentiometer, a volume control, a volume indicating meter, rheostat for controlling the photo-cell exciter lamp current and meters for reading the photo-cell exciter lamp current. The volume control, while located on the input control panel physically, actually is connected as a part of the voltage amplifier unit. This volume control consists of a specially built variable rheostat which is connected across the output of the second stage of the amplifier. The volume is controlled by varying the amount of resistance connected across the circuit. Since the resistance is non-inductive, the volume is controlled without affecting the quality of reproduction. The volume indicating meter is an instrument which is connected across the output of the voltage amplifier unit and the scale reading indicates the actual output of the amplifier. The photo-cell lamp current rheostats are resistors placed in the line to limit the current drawn by the lamp.

Power Amplifier Unit. Each power amplifier unit consists of a single stage of two UX-250 Radiotrons operating push-pull. Filament current is supplied by the low voltage winding of a power transformer and plate voltages are supplied by a full wave rectifier utilizing two UX-281 Radiotrons. The output of the power amplifier unit is matched to four 12-inch dynamic cone loud-speakers. The field current for these loud-speakers is supplied by a copper oxide rectifier which is fed from a separate winding on the power amplifier. These units are built with a filter system which effectively prevents any hum in the loud-speakers. Each power amplifier is designed to operate at 100 volts and the line voltage is reduced to this value by means of a suitable resistor mounted in the power amplifier control panel. This control panel also contains a meter which indicates line voltage, a separate line switch for each power amplifier and a monitor jack for each power amplifier. These last mentioned jacks are provided so that the monitoring loud-speaker may be connected across the output of any particular amplifier to check up on the quality of reproduction.

Voltage Amplifier Unit. The voltage amplifier unit used in RCA Photophone equipments Type "B" (SPU), "C" and "D" in a 3-stage transformer coupled push-pull amplifier employing six UX-210 Radiotrons. Filament voltage is supplied by a storage battery and the plate voltage is supplied by standard heavy duty radio "B" batteries, at 133 volts potential. These "B," batteries are located inside the amplifier within a metal cabinet. The output of the voltage amplifier unit is connected to the power amplifier unit through the voltage amplifier control panel. This panel contains a test meter and jacks for measuring the various voltages. On the Types "B" (SPU) and "C" this panel also contains switching arrangements for shifting from one voltage amplifier unit to the other. This panel also contains a switch for turning the voltage amplifier on and off.

Battery Charging Equipment. The storage batteries are supplied in duplicate, one set to be charged while the other is being used. Where there is alternating current supply available a Tungar or Rectigon charger will be used for charging these batteries. Where direct current supply is available a motor-generator set will be supplied. This unit will be equipped with a rheostat for controlling the charging rate, a voltmeter for indicating the voltage output and an ammeter to show

FIG. 93

the actual charging rate. There will also be included a reverse current relay to prevent the discharge of the batteries through the generator in case the motor-generator set is shut down.

Power Supply. Where 110 volt, 60 cycle alternating current power is available this line will be run direct to the amplifier through suitable fuses. If only direct current supply is available, converting equipment will be installed. This convertor is a standard direct-to-alternating-current machine with the exception that it has a special winding whereby, with an input of 125 volts direct current, the output is approximately 125 volts alternating current. For the larger equipment two of these convertors are installed, one to be used as standby equipment.

Projector Motors. RCA Photophone projectors are supplied with two types of motors. Likewise standard projectors which are equipped with RCA Photophone sound attachments are fitted with these motors. For direct current drive, a speed-regulated motor is used. This motor is installed with a set of resistors in the field circuit. Inside the motor itself there is a governor which is set by means of a dial on the end of the motor. When the motor is running this governor operates in a manner similar to the standard fly ball governor. There is a contractor which shorts out a portion of the field resistance when the speed rises above the desired value. This causes the motor to slow down, thus opening the contact. As soon as the contact is opened the increased field resistance causes the motor to increase its speed and the operation is repeated. The amount of resistance in the field circuit is controlled by a selector switch for high and low speeds and intermediate speeds are obtained by changing the adjusting of the governor and causing it to make contact at different speeds.

For alternating current installations the projectors are driven by synchronous motors in order to obtain absolutely constant speed for sound reproduction.

MOVIETONE

Mr. E. I. Sponable who has been associated with Mr. Case over a period of years, and who is now the technical expert for Fox-Case Movietone, read a paper on the "Technical Aspects of the Movietone" before the society of Motion Picture Engineers, the following is taken from that paper which was published in the S.M.P.E. Transactions:

The present recording rooms at the Fox-Case Studios were designed from experience gained in the construction of three previous experimental studios, the study of some of the modern broadcasting rooms, and through experiments relating to acoustical materials. It was decided that at least two separate recording studios were necessary. These rooms were constructed sound proof from street noises and from each other. It is possible to have sets being prepared on one stage while recordings are being made on the other.

The sound proofing is accomplished either by using very thick masonry walls or by using a double wall with an air space and a sound absorbing material within. The inner walls of our studios are made with 4-inch solid gypsum block, 1 inch of hair felt, 3 inches of air space, and another 4-inch solid gypsum block wall. These walls are started about 6 inches down in the concrete foundation. The outer walls are made of brick and masonry and are about 24 inches in thickness. A double ceiling is supported from the roof trusses. It is made of concrete plaster and separated by a 3-inch air space and 1-inch hair felt. The floors of the studios are covered with soft carpet. The inner walls

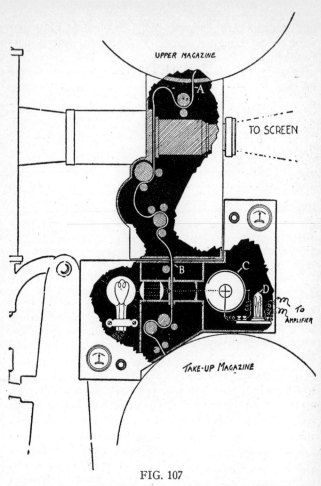

UPPER MAGAZINE

TO SCREEN

TAKE-UP MAGAZINE

TO AMPLIFIER

FIG. 107

MOVIETONE FILM A, FROM THE MAGAZINE AT THE TOP, PASSES
BEFORE THE PROJECTING LENS, THEN DOWN THROUGH THE
REGULATING SPROCKETS AND ROLLERS ENTERS MOVIETONE
CHAMBER AT B. C IS THE PHOTO-ELECTRIC CELL AND D THE
DETECTOR TUBE.

and ceilings are covered with Celotex and further damped by hanging heavy Monk cloth drapes perpendicular to the walls and ceiling. These drapes are arranged for raising and lowering, so that the degree of resonance may be varied to meet different conditions of recording.

This special arrangement of damping was found to be equivalent to covering the walls with 3 or 4 inches of hair felt and possessed the advantage over felt that the absorption of the sound was quite independent of frequency.

A small and a large stage have been equipped in the manner described. The small stage is 22 feet wide by 56 feet long by 21 feet high and is highly damped. This condition is used mainly when recording speech. In the case of musical numbers, a certain amount of resonance is preferable. Such conditions have been satisfied in the larger stage, which is 50 feet wide by 80 feet long by 21 feet high. The size of this stage permits the erection of sets for practically all types of present picture requirements. It is also used in recording the musical scores in synchronism with regular pictures. In this work the picture is projected on a screen from a sound proof booth, and the conductor of a selected orchestra follows the pictures, synchronizing such special effects as the score requires, often incorporating many things that promote the proper presentation of the picture and which would be difficult even in the larger theatre orchestras and practically impossible for the smaller theatres. The sound from the orchestra is recorded on a film running in synchronism with the projection machine. The sound negative so obtained can then be developed and combined with the regular picture negative to make positive prints having the Movietone scoring on the same film adjacent to the picture.

In designing the Fox-Case Studios, considerable thought was given to the problem of ventilation. The problem was more complicated than the usual ventila-

Courtesy Bell & Howell Co.

FIG. 108

MOTOR DRIVEN BELL & HOWELL CAMERA AS USED BY MOVIETONE.

tion problem due to the necessity of excluding blower and machinery noises. The air in the present studios is conditioned and is completely changed every eight minutes. The temperature and humidity of the rooms are controlled and held proper for maximum comfort.

This installation has proved well worth while in obtaining a higher efficiency from both artists and working personnel. This is especially noticeable in the picture scoring work, where large orchestras are playing over a period of several hours a day.

The picture lighting used in the sound studios is similar to that employed in regular motion picture work. Both hard and soft lights are used. In some cases it was found necessary to quiet down the operating mechanisms and also to change the reflectors in the Cooper-Hewitt lamps to prevent sound reflections. It is probable that later incandescent or improved lighting equipment and panchromatic film will help solve noise problems.

All of this work of adjusting acoustics in studios would not be necessary if the sound collectors used in recording could be made to act like our ears. Unfortunately, this has not been done and we find the microphone collecting sound in a manner quite similar to what one hears with one ear alone. This condition, together with the fact that in reproduction we usually require little if any more resonance in addition to that possessed by the theatre itself, makes the technique of microphone placing an art in itself and something that has a most important bearing on the illusion that will be obtained in the reproduced sound.

Sound collectors of the electrostatic or condenser type are employed. This apparatus, together with the auxiliary amplifier equipment necessary to increase the electrical energy picked up by the microphone corresponding to sound variations to a level necessary to operate the recording mechanism at the film, is practically Western Electric standard Public Address equipment.

In recording, it is necessary, of course, that the microphone be either placed outside of the camera field or masked. The intensity of sound varies inversely as the square of the distance, thus the problem of suitable position of the microphone is of utmost importance,

Courtesy Bell & Howell Co.

FIG. 109

BELL & HOWELL CAMERA AS USED BY FOX-CASE MOVIETONE
SHOWING SOUND RECORDING TUBE.

especially when recording weak sounds. In recording large orchestras and complex musical organizations, the balance of sound must be carefully adjusted through the use of a Monitor system. This system of monitoring is a replica of the standard reproducing system and thus enables one to judge at all times how the reproduced record should sound.

Two methods of changing the electrical variations, corresponding to original sound, into variations in light intensity and subsequent exposure of the photographic emulsion are being successfully used in Movietone recording. One of these consists in modulating what is known as a "light valve." The other method involves what is termed the "flashing lamp" principle and consists in modulating an electrical discharge taking place between electrodes in an actinic gas. This gas discharge device is a development made at the Case Research Laboratory and is termed "Aeo" light.

It is fairly simple to make a glow lamp, but to make a light that will follow all the intricacies of the different sounds, from the faintest to the loudest, and do this without distortion and, further, give sufficient light to properly expose a photographic film, has proved an interesting problem. Thus far the "Aeo" light has proved most satisfactory for this purpose. It consists of a glass or quartz bulb about $1\frac{1}{8}$ inches in diameter and 6 inches long. Two electrodes are mounted close to the rounded end of the bulb. One of these electrodes, the anode, is usually made of sheet nickel about $\frac{1}{8}$ inch wide and $\frac{1}{4}$ inch long. This is mounted opposite a U-shaped cathode of platinum coated with a mixture of alkaline earth oxides. During the manufacture of the "light" the oxide coated loop is activated, and a gas consisting mainly of helium is placed in the bulb at a pressure required to produce a concentrated glow about the cathode under an applied potential of about 350 volts and a current of about 10 milliamperes.

In use for sound recording, the "Aeo" light is maintained luminous by an exciting battery. Sound currents are superimposed on this luminous discharge causing it to modulate and vary in intensity in accordance with the original variations.

To print the sound image on the negative film, the "Aeo" light is inserted in a tube carrying a quartz slit mounted on a mechanical float, which presses very lightly against the film at the feed sprocket in the camera. The development of this slit was a very important step leading to the making of commercial sound records. The early inventors attempted to use a slit made up of metal knife edges. This was impractical due to the fact it could not be made sufficiently accurate for good sound recording and when placed against the film could not be kept free of dirt. The present slit consists of a small piece of quartz about 0.2 inches square and 20 mils thick. One surface of this piece is coated with a silver film and a slit is ruled in this film having dimensions of 0.10 inch $\times$ 0.0006 inch. A cover glass is then cemented upon the silver and this cover glass polished down so that the thickness of the cover over the slit, including the cement, is less than one one-thousandth of an inch thick. The "Aeo" light is mounted directly back of the slit and as close as physically possible. This type of slit has been successfully used for both recording and reproducing. It is now being superseded by an optical slit wherein the image of the slit ruled on the silvered quartz is focused upon the photographic film. The sound is recorded on standard negative film adjacent to the picture. The speed of the film during recording is 90 feet per minute.

During the development of this system it was considered desirable to adhere to standard equipment whenever possible, and this is especially true in the choice of camera equipment. In the studio, the cameras are

driven by synchronous motors. For portable work, 30
volt direct current motors are used with rheostat control
operated from storage batteries or special spring motors
controlled by a governor similar to those of phonograph motors. Fig. 108 shows a general view of a motor-driven studio camera. Fig. 109 shows the method
of threading the film and the sound recording tube in
position.

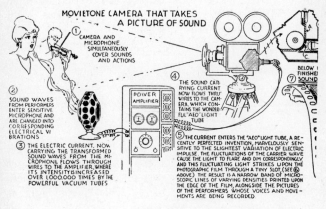

FIG. 110

A complete field recording outfit consists essentially
of a microphone, a special amplifier containing a volume
indicator, the "Aeo" light circuit, and a special sound
camera. Power for the amplifier is supplied by a 12-
volt storage battery and a 400-volt dry cell B Battery.
The outfit is transported in a ¾ ton automobile truck
and manned by a crew consisting of a camera man and
a sound man.

Processing. The processing of the film is being car-

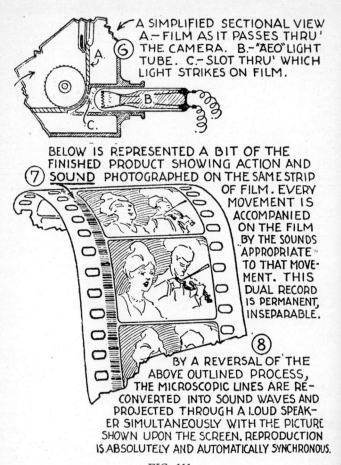

A SIMPLIFIED SECTIONAL VIEW
A.- FILM AS IT PASSES THRU'
THE CAMERA. B.-"AEO" LIGHT
TUBE. C.- SLOT THRU' WHICH
LIGHT STRIKES ON FILM.

BELOW IS REPRESENTED A BIT OF THE
FINISHED PRODUCT SHOWING ACTION AND
SOUND PHOTOGRAPHED ON THE SAME STRIP
OF FILM. EVERY
MOVEMENT IS
ACCOMPANIED
ON THE FILM
BY THE SOUNDS
APPROPRIATE
TO THAT MOVE-
MENT. THIS
DUAL RECORD
IS PERMANENT,
INSEPARABLE.

BY A REVERSAL OF THE
ABOVE OUTLINED PROCESS,
THE MICROSCOPIC LINES ARE RE-
CONVERTED INTO SOUND WAVES AND
PROJECTED THROUGH A LOUD SPEAK-
ER SIMULTANEOUSLY WITH THE PICTURE
SHOWN UPON THE SCREEN. REPRODUCTION
IS ABSOLUTELY AND AUTOMATICALLY SYNCHRONOUS.

FIG. 111

ried out in our regular commercial laboratory. The negative is developed by rack and tank method for normal time in a fine grain developer. The printing of the positive is at present accomplished by standard Bell & Howell semi-automatic continuous printers of the back shutter type. These are modified by installing masks at the printing aperture to allow for covering the sound track while the picture is being printed and vice versa. The negative and positives are then run through the printer twice. In printing, the sound is shifted with reference to the picture to provide proper synchronism on projection. In the camera, the distance from centre of picture with the intermittent about to move, to the sound slit is $7\frac{3}{4}$ inches, the sound slit being on the take-up side. In the projector this distance is increased to $14\frac{1}{2}$ inches.

In the developing of the positive and negative films, it has been found that contrast and consequently the quality of the reproduced sound follow the conditions necessary for good picture reproduction; namely, that the product of the negative and positive gammas be nearly unity. Fortunately for commercial purposes, these limits are not particularly narrow. It is more important for good quality of reproduction that the transmission of the sound record be correct. All laboratory work is gradually being placed on a mechanically and scientifically controlled basis. This will not only promote the production of better sound records but will improve the picture value as well.

Recording the picture and sound upon the same film make it possible to cut and edit the film in a manner very similar to that used for cutting pictures without sound records. Either the positive or negative can be handled in this manner.

Reproducing. The process of reproducing the sound from the Movietone film consists essentially in moving the sound record through a linear beam of light. The modulations in the form of sound lines on the film vary the light beam in accordance with the recorded sound. These light variations falling upon a photo-electric cell produce corresponding electrical variations which may be amplified and changed back into sound variations at the loud speaker to give the reproduction of the original sound.

The Movietone attachment for reproducing the sound has been designed to be applied to the standard Simplex projector and is placed between the head and the lower magazine. It consists of an accurately cut sprocket used to move the film at a uniform velocity between an aperture plate and tension shoe. A 25-watt, 12-volt straight coil filament lamp is focused upon a slit 1.5 mils wide. The image of this slit is then focused upon the sound track on the film at the aperture plate, giving a rectangle of light 0.080 inch×0.001 inch. The modulated light passing through the film falls upon a potassium photo-electric cell. This cell is connected to a three tube resistance coupled amplifier which is in turn coupled to a Standard Public Address amplifier system and loud speakers. Uniform motion of the sound sprocket is obtained by placing a rather heavy fly wheel on the shaft supporting the sprocket and driving the shaft through a damped spring mechanical filter system by a tuned motor generator drive.

For the smaller theatres a simplified attachment is used. The tuned motor generator drive is replaced by a synchronous motor or a direct current motor with rheostat control. The motor is belted to the fly wheel of the attachment by an endless cord belt which serves as a mechanical filter of motor pulses and does away with the spring filter mentioned above. The inertia of the fly wheel smooths out any gear inequalities that tend to reflect back from the head mechanism of the projector. In this simpler attachment a barium photoelectric cell picks up the sound variations and is coupled to the main amplifier through a one stage amplifier.

A number of sizes and arrangements of equipment are available to take care of all conditions of projection from the largest theatre down to the smallest demonstration room. These are made to operate either on direct current or alternating current as the conditions require.

In reproducing sound film it is of course necessary that the speed of the film be the same as that used in recording. The standard adopted for all Movietone film is 90 feet per minute. The fact that the sound and picture are on the same film means that synchronism and correct correlation of picture and sound are automatically taken care of. If the film is broken or parts are cut out, the sound and picture are equally affected.

BRISTOLPHONE

THE design and development of the apparatus necessary for making and reproducing talking motion pictures covered several fields of engineering science. Phonograph recording has always been a more or less secret process carried on behind locked doors. The knowledge and experience for doing finished work were confined to the larger phonograph companies. It was soon realized that acoustic recording for talking pictures, with a horn, would be impracticable because the person to be recorded would have to be very close to the horn in order to register, and the horn could not be concealed in the picture.

The development of the present electrical recording system, consisting of a high-quality microphone and amplifier apparatus, became available when the vacuum tube had been perfected to its present reliable and efficient form. The use of the microphone and amplifier allows for more latitude than the older system of horn recording, as well as affords a method of reproduction of a superior and more natural quality of the sound, which is largely due to the fact that the microphone may be highly damped in order to give a uniform frequency response; its relatively minute output may then be highly amplified and applied to a greatly damped recording device driven by the amplified energy.

Motion picture technique is well known and requires no attention here. The problem of synchronizing the sound record and the photographic image is the vital one. It would be impracticable to attempt rigidly to fasten the recording machine with its delicate devices directly to the camera. The synchronizing system which has been developed for driving the camera and the recording machine, and also for reproducing the sound record with the motion picture, consists of two special synchronizers, one of which generates the electrical energy in its magnetic field to feed the field of the other. The rotors or armatures of both synchronizers are energized from an alternating-current line. When the armature of one of the synchronizers is turned by an outside source of power, the armature of the other synchronizer turns the same amount and at the same speed. Torque is developed from rest with these synchronizers, thus making it possible to transmit power electrically from one synchronizer to the other, and with perfect synchronism.

Having recorded synchronously the sound on a phonograph record and the action on a motion picture film, the next problem to be solved was the reproduction of the picture on the screen in perfect synchronism with the sound of the record.

We realized quickly that the reproduction of the sound must be electrical in character, with a loud-speaking telephone near the screen, and with the turn-table located in the booth, by the projector, for the convenience of the operator. A carbon granule phonograph reproducer was made, using a battery for energizing the carbon granules, which developed considerably more volume than the phonograph of the earlier date. This device has passed through gradual development and now affords a very simple electrical reproducer without vacuum tube amplification.

Inherent limitations in the carbon granule device have resulted in a further development of a high-quality electro-magnetic pick-up. An amplifier and loud speaker have been developed to complete the sound-reproducing system.

In the exhibition of the talking motion pictures the film is started at a marked point at the beginning of the film, and the reproducing needle is ingated in the beginning of the first groove, this groove being eccentric and easy to locate.

When the complete apparatus is set into operation, the picture and sound will be in perfect synchronism and will stay so throughout the length of the film record.

In actual service, films are often injured and sections cut off. In making repairs care should be taken to replace pieces of film of the same lengths as the parts that have been cut out, so that perfect synchronism will be maintained. In order to provide against errors that might be made in making repairs of the film, or, possibly, to provide against an error in locating the starting-point of the film in the projector, or in setting the needle on the starting-point of the record, a unique resynchronizing method has been devised. By means of this method the film may be advanced or retarded with respect to the sound record, even during the projection of the pictures, without affecting the quality of the sound reproduction.

Thus, we have a perfect synchronizing system which affords opportunity of making corrections for any possibility of imperfect lengths of film or permits the operator to make corrections for accidental errors in starting—all without stopping the performance.

This unique feature is accomplished by mounting the field winding frame of one of the synchronizers in trunnion bearings within which the armature bearings are located, thus allowing the field frame of one of the synchronizers to be rotated with reference to its armature independently of the rotation of the armature.

When one of the armatures is revolved at a given speed, its speed with reference to its field can be changed by rotating manually the field frame in its trunnion bearings. Ordinarily, when transmitting power from one of the synchronizers to the other the field frames are stationary, and the speed of the second armature will be the same as that of the first. If the field frame of the first synchronizer is rotated, the speed of the second armature will be the same as the new speed of the first armature relative to its field, and not the actual speed of the first armature.

Success in originally producing synchronized phonograph records and motion pictures depends upon the use of electrical synchronization so that the phonograph record of the sound may be made at any desired distance away from the motion picture camera. However, in the reproduction of the phonograph records synchronously with the projection of the pictures on the screen, systems of direct mechanical connection between the phonograph turn-table and the projector are being used today. These directly mechanically connected turn-tables and projectors do not afford any opportunity for re-synchronization without introducing differential gearing, or some mechanical equivalent which would be more or less complicated and tend to introduce vibrations which would seriously affect the perfect reproduction of the sounds, especially of music.

It will be seen that the electrical synchronizers which have been previously described afford ideally simple means for re-synchronizing. A striking feature of the working of the two synchronizers is that their action is not affected by considerable variation of the voltage, or of the frequency, of the alternating current by which the rotors are energized.

When in 1915 application was made for a patent on the synchronizers for synchronizing phonograph records and motion pictures, it was discovered that the fundamental principle involved had been patented previously by Dr. Carl J. A. Michalke, of Berlin, for the purpose of indicating and transmitting motion to a distant point.

Fig. 113 is a diagrammatic representation of two synchronizers. The rotors, or armatures, R and R', are fed from the alternating-current line as indicated, while the field windings A, B, C and A', B', C' are interconnected, as shown by wires D, E and F.

Assume that the power is to be transmitted from the rotor, or armature, R to R'. When the alternating current is turned on, both rotors will instantly take corresponding positions with reference to the field windings A, B, C and A', B', C'. In the position of the rotors as shown in Fig. 113, the rotor R is inducing voltage in its field windings A, B and C. The voltage in B being at its maximum, since the lines of magnetic flux are parallel to the axis of the core at the rotor. In A and C the induced voltages are equal but each less than in B. These voltages are transmitted through the wires D, E and F to their corresponding windings A', B', C', thus producing three magnetic forces acting on the armature R', which will hold it in an equilibrium position as if the rotors were electrically geared together.

If a source of power is applied to rotor R, revolving it through an angle in a clockwise direction, the voltage induced in the field coil B will decrease to a point of no voltage after the rotor R has turned through an angle of 90°, bringing the magnetic lines of the rotor R

perpendicular to those of the field coil B. In the meantime the voltage of the field coil C has decreased to no voltage and has begun to increase toward the maximum. In the coil A the induced voltage has passed through the maximum point and has begun to decrease. From this it will be seen that as the rotor R is revolved, maximum voltages are induced in its field coils one after the other in a counter-clockwise rotation exactly corre-

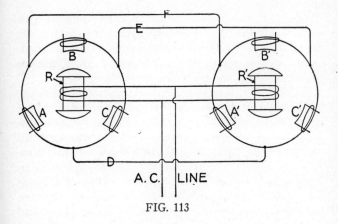

FIG. 113

sponding in rate to the rotation of the rotor R in a clockwise direction.

It will be readily understood that the varying voltages induced in the field coils A, B and C will be transmitted through the wires D, E, F to the corresponding field coils A', B', C', where they will cause corresponding magnetic forces on the rotor, or armature, R', which will make it revolve exactly as rotor R is revolved and with power corresponding to the electrical energy induced in the field coils.

The amount of power which it is possible to transmit with synchronizers of this kind is not limited, but depends upon the size, mechanical construction and electrical energy supplied to the rotors. In the present application, the synchronizers are made to transmit as much as one-quarter horsepower and are about the same size as a modern quarter horsepower electric motor.

Fig. 113 may also be used to explain the fundamental principles of re-synchronization.

Suppose the field A, B, C is rotated one revolution in the same direction as its armature R, while the armature itself has turned through ten revolutions, the armature R will actually have turned only nine revolutions with reference to the field A, B, C. The rotor R' will therefore only have turned nine revolutions, although R has actually revolved ten revolutions.

Again, suppose the field A, B, C is turned one revolution in a direction opposite to that of its armature R, while the armature itself has turned through ten revolutions. The result will be that the armature R has made eleven revolutions with respect to its field A, B, C and the armature R' will then have made eleven turns, although the armature R has actually made only ten revolutions.

The mechanical and electrical structure of the pick-up is shown in Fig. 114. The armature A is supported by the torsion suspension T, so as to be held equidistant from the pole pieces, P, P. The needle is secured to the armature by the set screw S and movements of the needle displace the armature around the torsional axis T, increasing and decreasing the gaps between it and the lower pole pieces, thus changing the magnetic flux in the armature.

There is practically no motion of the armature in the upper gaps, the lower gaps being the active ones.

The rubber pads, *D*, furnish damping for the armature. A main feature of the construction of this pick-up is its ruggedness and reliability as the armature

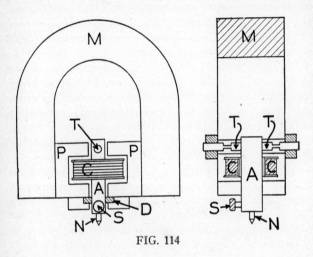

FIG. 114

is maintained exactly centrally between the pole pieces by the torsion suspension *T*.

A special amplifier has been designed for use with this electro-magnetic pick-up.

VITAPHONE

THE operation of Vitaphone equipment naturally divides itself into two parts, (1) recording, and (2) reproducing. Briefly, the operation of recording equipment is as follows:

First, the set is prepared to meet all of the requirements for ordinary motion pictures in the usual manner. This, of course, must be done in a studio which is acoustically suitable, i.e., free from extraneous noise during the recording, and not subject to objectionable reverberations or echoes. The microphones are placed so as to pick up in a proper volume the sounds which it is desired to record. The film in the camera behind the shutter is marked, the recording wax is placed on the turn-table and the inter-locking electrical drive which maintains synchronism between the camera and the recorder is energized.

The recorder is lowered onto the wax disc and the motor started, and the act produced. The sound recording is affected from the center of the disc to the periphery instead of the reverse as in the case of commercial phonograph records. In order to insure proper amplitude, and to insure high quality, the recording is observed under a microscope during the process. The beginning of the cut on the inside of the record is marked by an arrow which will indicate the starting point of the record for reproduction.

During all of the time that recording is taking place, a monitoring system is in use. This consists of a loud speaker and auxiliary apparatus, by means of which it is possible for the engineers to check up on the quality of the electrical "sound" fluctuations that are being de-

livered to the recording mechanism and so to eliminate
quickly any defects in pick-up, transmission or amplification.

Courtesy Bristolphone Corp.

FIG. 115

COMPLETE BRISTOLPHONE OUTFIT WITH THE SYNCHRONIZING
MOTOR INSTALLED ON A SIMPLEX PROJECTOR.

At the time that the sound record is being made in the recording room, the pictures are being taken in the studio. The cameras are run by synchronous motors operated on the same circuit as a similar motor that turns the disc in the recording room. Because of this electrical linkage of the parts, the making of the pictures and of the sound record is always in step—synchronized, in a word.

Before the actual work is started, the camera is threaded with film, a marked frame being put in place in the camera gate. The recording stylus is set at marked point on the record and the two motors are started from rest and run to synchronization. An elaborate signaling system between the attendant at the recording machine, the director and the camera man enables each one to know just what the others are doing.

In order to keep a check on the synchronization of the mechanism, two forms of stroboscopes are used. In one case, this takes the form of a disc about two and one-half inches in diameter divided into several parts, like slices of pie. These are colored alternately black and white. A neon tube operating on the same alternating current as the rest of the apparatus, sheds its light on the disc. The light pulsates in accord with the fluctuations of its actuating current, although these fluctuations are invisible to the naked eye. If synchronization is correct, the whirling disc will appear to the eye of the attendant to be stationary. This is because of the fluctuations of the light falling on the disc, and the relationship of the speed of these changes to the size of the divisions on the disc and the disc's speed.

A similar stroboscope is attached to the camera-driving mechanism. Another type also is used at the recording end, wherein the edge of the turn-table is divided into black and white sections that appear to the eye to be stationary under the proper conditions.

In reproduction the film is placed in the machine, the starting frame on the film which is marked "START" with the designating number of the film, is placed exactly in the centre of the aperture of the motion picture machine when the shutter is in the open position. The corresponding sound record is placed on the turn-table with the needle of the reproducer opposite the arrow on the inside groove. With the film and record thus set, the amplifiers should now be turned on, the potentiometer set to give the desired volume, projector light turned on and the starting switch on the control box operated. This starts both records simultaneously and the show is on.

In the projection of these pictures and their accompanying sounds, the process of synchronization is very simple. The turntable carrying the disc is on the same motor shaft that drives the mechanism of the projector. Again a marker on the film is put in its proper position, the stylus of the reproducer is placed by its own mark and the motor is started. Here it is impossible to lose synchronization.

It is interesting to note that the record in this work is used in just the reverse manner from that of an ordinary phonograph. The stylus travels in the groove from the centre of the record to the outer edge. According to one of the engineers of the Vitaphone Corporation, this is done because it is found that the stylus "tracks" better and a more accurate record is obtained in this way.

The Vitaphone equipment installed in connection with

a Simplex projector consists of a motor used for driving the projector and the turn-table, it is designed to operate on 110 volts DC or AC commercial service, and is provided with a special circuit by means of which the speed of the machine is maintained at 1,200 R.P.M.

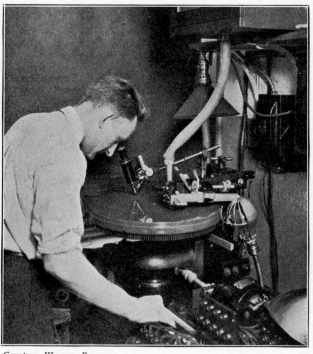

Courtesy Warner Bros.

FIG. 118

RECORDING SOUND ON A DISC RECORD. MICROSCOPES ARE USED BY THE RECORDING EXPERTS TO WATCH THE RECORDS AS THE MUSIC OR VOICE IS RECORDED.

It is mounted on a substantial base, supported by three telescoping legs by means of which its height may be adjusted. The control circuit is contained in a steel box, and is connected to the motor by a multi-conductor cable encased in flexible conduit. A special 1/5 H.P. shunt or repulsion type motor is furnished together with its control circuit, according to whether the power supply is a nominal 110 volts DC or AC.

This equipment consists of a drive or gear box mounted on the same base as the motor and coupled directly to the shaft of the motor, a vertical extensible shaft equipped with universal joints and a second drive which is a bevel gear box and replaces the speed regulator of the projector machine. By means of these two sets of gears the speed is reduced from a motor speed of 1,200 R.P.M. to a speed on the projection machine shaft of 90 R.P.M., which corresponds to a film speed of 90 feet per minute.

On the opposite end of the motor from the projector driving mechanism is the turn-table equipment. The turn-table mechanism is mounted on a heavy telescoping pedestal base, the three supporting legs of which are provided with adjusting screws so that it may be leveled. A worm gear mechanism is housed in a casting in the top of the pedestal. The shaft of the worm projects outward, and is connected to the driving motor shaft through a flexible coupling designed to prevent the transmission of vibrations from the motor to the turn-table. The gear wheel which meshes with the worm carries a vertical shaft on which the turn-table disc is mounted. Between the gear wheel and the vertical shaft of the turn-table is a mechanical filter or "shock-absorber" consisting of light springs designed to prevent the transmission of gear noises from the worm gear to the turn-table and thence to the record and reproducer. The worm gear ratio is such as to reduce the speed from 1,200 R.P.M. to 33 1/3 R.P.M., which is the correct turn-table speed.

CINEPHONE

THE Powers Cinephone is a sound reproducer for all "sound-on-film" systems such as Movietone, and R. C. A. Photophone, the attachment may easily and quickly be installed on any Simplex projector, and special adjustments make it possible to be attached to almost any projector made.

FIG. 120
253

Courtesy Powers Cinephone

FIG. 122

The amplifier is of the "dual" type, it is really two amplifiers in one cabinet and so wired that the operator may switch over from one to the other in case of trouble. The Main Amplifier cabinet holds the complete battery equipment, this equipment consists of two small storage batteries and a set of dry batteries. The battery charger is also located in this cabinet. The cabinet requires a floor space of 23x13 inches. Fig. 120 shows the Cinephone sound-on-film reproducing attachment mounted directly under the projector head. Fig. 122 is a view of the reproducer showing the reproducing lamp.

FIG. 124

SIMOTONE REPRODUCER.

SIMOTONE

THE Simotone is a low cost recording and reproducing system using the disc method of sound synchronization. The system was developed by Louis J. Simon.

The Simotone records and reproduces at the standard speed of 33 1/3-90 and the system is interchangeable with the Western Electric System. Both the recorder and reproducer are simple, the synchronization of the disc record turntable with the projector is accomplished by a driving sprocket on the projector, which is placed between the upper film magazine and the upper sprocket of the projector.

The attachment for the projector sits on top of the projector mechanism and it is not necessary to change the position of any of the projector parts or the motor when installing the sound attachment. Fig. 124 is a photograph of the Simotone, in this photograph it will be seen that the driving shaft, connecting the projector head with the record turntable, is in one piece, the driving sprocket being on the projector end and the worm gears on the other, since this photograph was made, a change has been made, the driving shaft now comes in two sections, these two sections being connected by a compensating device which takes up any vibrations transmitted to the projector, this makes for steady operation of the turntable pick-up.

The recording apparatus is portable and compact, it is easily transported for use on outside locations.

The amplifying device used is that made by the Columbia Co., using the Kolster commercial amplifier.

PHONOFILM

Dr. Lee De Forest's Phonofilm was one of the first of the "sound picture" systems to reach Broadway, but when first presented failed to find public favor, this was due we believe to the type of subjects presented. Both in the recording and reproducing of the sound picture the method employed is similar to that of the Fox-Case Movietone, the sound record being photographed on the margin of the motion picture film, by means of the photo-electric cell.

De Forest has used two types of photo-electric cells in the Phonofilm system, he first employed the so-called Kuntze, potassium-mirror, photo-electric cell, but later used the "Thallafide" cell. This is the cell perfected by Theodore W. Case and it was found that it was most sensitive to the infra-red and red radiations.

The "Thallafide" cell was used by the United States government in the Case system of secret signalling during the latter part of the world war, and is at present used in the Fox-Case Movietone.

There are many "talking movie" systems now available, including—Biaphone, Qualitone, Reeltone, Pacent Reproducer, Moviephone, Talkaphone and several others. It is unnecessary to deal with each of these systems, as it would only mean a repartition of text matter. For the most part they employ the disc record method. To those interested in any system not covered in this book, the writer will be pleased to furnish full particulars on request.

OPERATING INSTRUCTIONS FOR WESTERN ELECTRIC SOUND PROJECTOR SYSTEM

Cleaning Mechanism and Film. Strict cleanliness as regards both the film and the film pick-up mechanism is most important.

Dirt on the exciting lamp or on the lenses, or dirt clogging the openings in the aperture plate and tension pad, will lead to low volume and poor quality.

Dirt or emulsion accumulating on the film tracks of the aperture plate and tension pad may lead to scratching of the film.

Dirt on the sprocket in the film compartment may cause unsteady pitch in reproduction.

Dirt, dust, oil, fingermarks, scratches or sprocket-hole cracks on the film will cause noisy operation.

The film must therefore be kept in first-class condition, and the different parts mentioned must be cleaned at least once every day.

A pipe cleaner and tooth-brush should be used for cleaning the sprocket and tension pad. Dust and surplus oil should be wiped off with a dry cloth. Do not scrape the film tracks with a knife or abrasive in cleaning them. The film tracks must always be perfectly smooth and polished to the touch. Run the finger tip over them at least once daily to see that no rough spots are developing due to dirt or emulsion hardening on.

Film should be cleaned by drawing it gently through clean, soft, cloths. Do not use chemicals or "dope" on it.

Sprocket-hole cracks in the film can be avoided by not having excessive tension on it. Use no more tension than is necessary to get a clear picture at the highest projection speed used in the house.

Adjusting Film Exciting Lamp. It is vitally important to have the exciting lamp of the film pick-up apparatus properly adjusted.

To light this lamp, set the film-disc switch on the front of the machine at "FILM." Then turn the control knob on the door of the exciting lamp compartment until the meter adjacent reads exactly 3.6 amperes. This value is important.

The object of this lamp is to produce a bright, clear illumination on the sound track of the film and on the photo-electric cell. The light from the lamp passes through the lens tube. In the side of this tube will be seen a small round window. Take out the removable partition between the lamp compartment and the film compartment, and swing the glare shield in place over the lamp, to avoid dazzling the eyes. Light the lamp; then on looking through the window in the lens tube, a narrow horizontal slit will be seen inside the tube, at the right. The light falling on this slit should be bright and sharply focused, with the slit in the centre. On removing the tension pad and holding a small white card or piece of paper in front of the aperture, an oval spot of light will be seen on the white surface. The edges of this spot will be soft and blurred, but otherwise it should be clear and uniform. There should not be shadows at the top or bottom or at the ends.

Check the two points just mentioned at least once every day. Whenever the illumination does not meet these requirements, adjust the lamp as will now be described.

The exciting lamp is mounted on a bracket. This bracket in turn is mounted on two supporting pieces, which also serve to make contact for the lamp circuit. The bracket can be removed by simply pulling it sideways. Four adjustments for the exciting lamp are provided on this bracket, namely:

Clamping Adjustment. The lamp base is held in a socket which is clamped by means of a thumbscrew. At the bottom of the socket is a spring contact stud. The lamp base has a pin in the side, and the socket is slotted to clear this pin. When putting in a lamp, see that the clamp screw is loosened, then push the lamp down until the pin is out of the slot, and turn it so that the pin locks it in place, like a bayonet joint. The lamp must always have the filament perpendicular to the length of the lens tube, that is, parallel with the film. Except when putting in a new lamp, this adjustment should not need attention.

Vertical Adjustment. Loosen the clamping screw of this adjustment, then by means of the adjusting screw move the lamp bracket up or down as required until the light is vertically centred on the slit in the lens tube. Tighten clamping screw.

Sideways Adjustment. Loosen the clamping screw of this adjustment, then by means of the adjusting screw move the lamp bracket sideways so as to centre the light on the slit horizontally. When trying to move bracket away from you, press steadily on the clamping screw at the same time; otherwise the bracket will not move. Finally tighten clamping screw.

Focusing Adjustment. Loosen the clamping screw of this adjustment, then turn the adjusting screw so as to get the sharpest possible focus of the light on the slit. Tighten clamping screw.

The filament image should now be bright and sharp and perfectly centred on the slit. Check the illumination in front of the aperture plate by means of the white card test. If the light spot shows any shadows at top or bottom or sides, move the lamp slightly up or down or sideways, as required, until these shadows disappear. Do not change the focus.

After an exciting lamp has been used considerably, the filament may show a tendency to sag. This has a bad effect on the volume, as the filament image no longer coincides with the slit. Another result of ageing that tends to cut down the volume is blackening of the lamp bulb, which reduces the amount of light emitted. Therefore, as soon as the filament begins to sag noticeably or the glass begins to darken, replace the lamp.

On account of the number of operations involved in adjusting the exciting lamp, and the possibility that one may have to be replaced during a show, it is very necessary to have some means of putting in a new lamp and operating it at a moment's notice. This can be done by setting up in the machine each spare lamp and bracket supplied, and making all bracket adjustments needed for proper operation.

Lubrication of Mechanism. The mechanism should be lubricated regularly. Avoid lubricating at irregular intervals and avoid using more lubricant than necessary. The excess lubricant does not last in the machine any longer than a moderate quantity; it simply runs off, clogs the mechanism, gets on the film, and spoils both the picture and the sound.

Driving Side of Machine. Apply one or two drops of light machine oil daily to the following parts:

Universal joints on vertical shaft, oil hole on upper gear box (projector drive gear box; with Simplex and Powers heads only), oil cup at right of flywheel, friction discs of lower magazine take-up (turn magazine reel by hand while doing this, to spread the oil), apply a small amount of graphite, grease or vaseline twice a week to the inner side of the driving chain, once each week clean the take-up friction surfaces by removing the discs and wiping the friction surfaces with a rag soaked in clean oil.

Operating Side of Machine. Apply one or two drops of light machine oil daily to the following parts:

Lowest guide roller in projection head, guide roller in film compartment (top roller), tension pad idler roller, top idler of film chute, bottom idlers of film chute, oil hole behind sprocket in lower magazine, pad roller in lower magazine, idler roller in lower magazine, oil hole behind take-up spindle in lower magazine. No lubrication by the projectionist is required for any of the equipment, beyond that just specified.

Starting Amplifier Equipment. When the 41-A, or 43-A amplifiers are installed, proceed as follows:

See that starting switches on 42-A and 43-A amplifiers are turned off and that horn safety switch is off. If starting up during a show make sure that theatre horns are turned off by means of output control key on output control panel. See that storage batteries are switched on ready for use. On DC supply, start motor

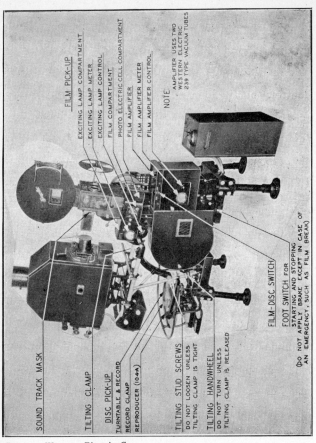

Courtesy Western Electric Co.

FIG. 128

OPERATING SIDE OF PROJECTOR EQUIPPED WITH WESTERN
ELECTRIC REPRODUCER.

generator. See that power safety switch is closed. If using film reproduction, set film-disc switch at "Film," and turn control knob on amplifier door so that adjacent meter reads 270 milliamperes. On 42-A and 43-A amplifiers turn starting switch to "Fil." On 41-A amplifier, see that filament key is on, and adjust filament control, so that filament meter reads 270 milliamperes. On 42-A and 43-A amplifiers, after allowing at least one minute to elapse since turning switch to "Fil," turn this switch to "Plate." On 41-A amplifier, press in turn the three buttons marked "Plate Current." Meter marked "Plate" should read in each case not less than 1.35 nor more than 1.55 milliamperes. On 42-A and 43-A amplifiers, each meter pointer should be on red mark. Turn on horn safety switch.

When the amplifier installed is the 46-B, proceed as follows: See that horn safety switch is off. If starting up during a show, make sure that theatre horns are turned off, by means of output key on amplifier. See that storage batteries are switched on ready for use. On DC supply, start motor generator. See that power safety switch is closed. If using film reproduction, set film-disc switch at "Film," and turn control knob on amplifier door so that adjacent meter reads 270 milliamperes.

On 46-B amplifier, turn on starting switch, and adjust filament control so that right-hand meter reads 270 milliamperes.

Check reading on left-hand meter on amplifier. It should be between 0.85 and 1.1 milliamperes. Reading on centre meter should be between 1.3 and 1.6 milliamperes. Press meter key; right-hand meter should now read between 50 and 65 milliamperes. Turn on horn safety switch.

Testing Amplifier Equipment. Having started up the amplifier equipment as already described, test it as follows before every show in which it will be used:

If both disc and film equipment is installed, switch in whichever is to be tested first, by means of the film-disc switch. Put pick-up equipment on one machine on turntable in circuit, by setting fader at point 9 on side to which this equipment is connected. If testing disc pick-up, rub needle of reproducer lightly with finger. This should be clearly heard in monitor horn.

If testing film pick-up, see that lamp current is at value previously specified, and readjust if necessary. Now take out tension pad and move a card up and down across light spot. Every time this is done a click should be heard in the monitor horn. Finally, replace light gate.

Move fader to other side and test that pick-up equipment in the same way. Bring fader to zero.

Shutting Down Amplifier Equipment. Proceed as follows:

Turn off horn safety switch. Turn off starting switches on 42-A and 43-A or 46 type amplifiers. Turn off power safety switch. On DC supply, also shut down motor-generator set. Set film-disc transfer switch at "Off" (if installation is equipped for film reproduction). Turn off storage batteries at battery panel.

Starting Mechanism and Testing System. Every day before the house opens test the theatre horns individually and at the same time check the operation of the projector and pick-up mechanism.

Regular daily testing is of great value and importance for the reason that a large proportion of failures and defects do not happen suddenly, but develop gradually, and hence can be detected and remedied before they become serious.

Keep a stock of two or three records or sound films especially for testing, independently of those used in

Courtesy Western Electric Co.

FIG. 129

DRIVING SIDE OF PROJECTOR.

the show. Piano, speech, and orchestra selections are the most suitable. At least two copies of each record or two prints of each film are required.

After cleaning and lubricating the mechanism, checking the exciting lamp, and starting and testing the amplifier equipment, start and test the mechanism and horns by proceeding as follows:

Turn off all theatre horns and if installation has an output control panel, providing an individual dial switch for each horn, set these controls at zero, that is, turned all the way to the right. Keep on monitor horn with control at usual setting.

On fader, set pointer at zero. If installation includes both film and disc reproduction, see that film-disc switch is set for type of pick-up which is to be tested.

On the two machines, set up two copies of one of test records, or thread two prints of one of the test films.

On each motor control box, see that regulator switch is set at "REG" and that starting switch is on.

Set up operator's and observer's telephone sets. The Manager, or some one else qualified to judge whether reproduction through theatre horns is satisfactory, should now go into theatre and stay within easy reach of observer's telephone.

Start first projector by raising foot switch on machine base.

Check reading of meter on control box. After machine is up to speed, reading should vary somewhere between 20 and 30 mils, on AC supply, or 40 and 60 mils, on DC supply.

See that projector mechanism is running freely and that disc reproducer is tracking properly and has not jumped any grooves, and that film is passing through smoothly.

Bring up fader pointer to one step below correct setting for record or sound film which is being played. Music or speech should now be heard from monitor horn.

If the installation has an output control panel, turn all theatre horns on and then off again, one at a time. The observer, who ought to be near the stage, should listen to each horn in turn and check its operation. He should also be sure that the sound from each horn is clear, free of noise, and of full volume.

Put on all horns, with fader at correct setting, and see that reproduction is satisfactory.

If installation includes an emergency amplifier equipment, switch over to this equipment by means of key or system switching panel, and see that reproduction is satisfactory, using all horns. Then switch back to regular arrangement.

Stop first machine by pressing down foot switch on machine base. With disc pick-up, put new needle in reproducer and set it back at starting point of record. With film pick-up, rewind film and set it back at starting point.

Now start both machines and compare outputs for volume and quality by switching from one pick-up to other on fader.

Put fader on zero, stop machines, and put away test records of films.

If the above tests are satisfactory, the equipment is ready for operation.

Setting Up. Film Reproduction. To set up a sound film ready for operation, proceed as follows:

See that fader is at zero and that film pick-up circuits are connected to it.

On projector head, place aperture sound track mask in position.

On projector, place framing lever in central position. Move projector mechanism by turning handwheel, so that shutter cut-off blade is uppermost, lens is open and intermittent has just ceased moving. Thread projector mechanism with film in usual manner except as follows:

For Simplex, be sure that loop between intermittent

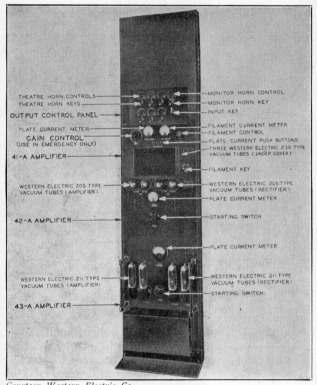

Courtesy Western Electric Co.

FIG. 130

OUTPUT CONTROL PANEL AND AMPLIFIERS.

sprocket and lower sprocket of head, is such that film just comes in line with edge of head.

For Motiograph, allow a tight "two finger" loop between intermittent sprocket and lower sprocket of head.

For Powers, thread above automatic loop-setter and allow a "two-finger" loop.

If using a type of projector head other than one of

Courtesy Western Electric Co.

FIG. 131

FRONT VIEW OF 46-B AMPLIFIER.

the three makes just mentioned, allow a length of film equal to 19 1/3 frames, or 14½″, between centre of picture aperture in the projector head, and centre of light-gate aperture in reproducing machine. In other words, if the frame centred at projector aperture is called No. 1, then, counting downwards along film, middle of light-gate aperture should be one-third of a frame past center of No. 20. This gives perfect syn-chronism between sound and picture with all makes of heads, and is basis of rules for threading just given.

Thread film through film reproducing mechanism. In doing this allow for slack, between lower sprocket of projector head and sprocket of film reproducing mech-anism, a length of film equal to approximately two sprocket tooth intervals.

After film has been properly located on reproducing machine sprocket, do not forget to release tension pad, so that it bears on film and holds it close up against aperture plate in front of lens tube. Door cannot be shut unless tension pad is released. Also close the film chute cover so as to have the film completely enclosed in case of fire.

Disc Reproduction. To set up the record and film ready for operation, proceed as follows:

See that fader is at zero and that disc pick-up circuits are connected to it.

See that reproducer is in its rest. Put in new needle.

Select film and record to be used, and be sure to check number on record against number on film. Mark record on label to show number of times used, counting this run.

On projector, place framing lever in central position. Move projector mechanism by turning handwheel so that shutter cut-off blade is uppermost, lens is open, and intermittent has just ceased moving. Thread pro-jector and reproducing mechanism with film in same manner as just described for film reproduction, placing frame marked "START" directly in front of aperture.

On Simplex and Motiograph, this step is easier if you remember that when a frame is in front of the aperture, the lower edge of the aperture plate track will be between the eighth and ninth sprocket holes from the lower edge of the frame. Therefore, splice a white leader on the ninth hole from the "START" frame, and then when you line up this splice with the lower edge of the aperture plate track, "START" frame will be at the aperture. On Powers, the gate is open when threading, so that there is no difficulty.

Set up record on turntable. In doing this, following method must be strictly observed so as to avoid risk of imperfect synchronism or damage to records. Motor must never be turned when adjusting record on turntable:

Hold record with both hands and lay it on turntable so that starting arrow is at about the place where needle comes. Wipe off record lightly with cleaner provided.

Pick up forward end of reproducer unit between thumb and forefinger of your left hand so that tips of thumb and finger project about ½″ below bottom of unit.

Move unit over until needle point is above starting groove and rest tips of thumb and forefinger on record surface so as to hold needle point just off record.

Place your right hand with fingers resting lightly on underside of turntable, near edge, and thumb on top of record, near edge; hold turntable steady and by moving thumb turn record so that starting arrow comes exactly below needle point.

Lower needle down gently into starting groove at this point by slowly opening thumb and forefinger between which it is held. Do not push point into groove by sliding it sideways across uncut record surface, but lower it straight down. When it is in place rest fingers lightly on top of reproducer and gently press it towards each side to make sure needle point is in groove.

Put record clamp over centre pin of turntable and press it down on record firmly, but not too heavily.

Turn over mechanism by handwheel until turntable and record have revolved about half a turn. See that needle tracks properly on record and film travels free.

On synchronized feature pictures, by starting and stopping motor with starting switch run off as much

Courtesy *Western Electric Co.*

FIG. 132

INTERIOR VIEW OF 46-B AMPLIFIER.

film as necessary to bring end of "Part No." leader approximately up to projector aperture. Avoid doing this to excess, as it tends to burn up the switch contacts.

Never attempt to stop or slow up a projector equipped for disc reproduction by holding on to the turntable, as this may cause damage to the apparatus and spoil the synchronism for the subject that is being set up. The turntable coasts about four turns after the power is shut off.

Never remove record clamp, or put it on, while turntable is revolving.

Running the Show. Before giving in detail the steps to be followed in running the show, some general points will be touched on.

Courtesy Western Electric Co.

FIG. 133

W. E. FADER.

Before any public showing, all presentations should be rehearsed.

The fader must always be kept at zero when the house is open, except when testing with all theatre horns turned off, or when voice or music is actually being reproduced, with the motor up to speed. This is necessary (a) to avoid the record surface noise or film noise being noticed (b) to prevent the possibility of noises being heard from the horns at times when the pick-up equipment is being handled (c) to preclude the voice or music being heard in distorted form when the motor is speeding up or slowing down, in case it has to be stopped during a reel from film breakage or other cause.

When making a change-over, move the fader as smoothly as possible, and if you cannot make a complete change-over in one movement, stop at zero for a fresh grip. Be careful not to overshoot the setting and then have to come back to it.

If the installation includes disc pick-up, always keep the reproducer in the rest except when a record is set up.

Under no circumstances is it permissible to run pictures with synchronized voice or music at any other speed than 90 ft. per minute—that is to say, when running such pictures the motor control box regulating switch must always be set at "REG," and never at "VAR." Any adjustment in the timing of the program by speeding up numbers or slowing them down must therefore be done elsewhere than in the synchronized reels.

So that the operator may have immediate and proper notification in case any part of the show is not coming over as it should, a member of the staff designated by the management, perhaps an usher, should remain in the theatre all through the performance. This observer should be competent to judge quality of reproduction, synchronism, etc.; he should be within reach of the observer's telephone and given responsibility for notifying the operator immediately anything goes wrong. He should also keep the operator informed as to how well the house is filled, so that the latter can adjust the volume if necessary.

Never make the monitor horn so loud that it can be heard outside the projection room; keep the volume up just enough to follow the sound after the numbers have started, and make it a little louder before cues.

Do not cut synchronized film or sound film except in case of breakage. If it is found desirable to eliminate bows at the end of the film, use the douser. If there is insufficient leader to permit proper threading of the film at starting, you may add more blank leader, provided, of course, it is added before the "START" mark. Leader must always be so added if it is found that the voice or music begins before the motor is fully up to speed.

If the machines are equipped with a safety device which stops the motor when the film has run through, then, with disc reproduction, in case the record does not end until some time after the finish of the film, this ending will be spoiled through the safety device shutting down the equipment, unless sufficient blank film is added at the end to keep this device from operating until the music is finished. Check this point during rehearsal and before running show make sure these blank lengths have been added to any reels that require them.

With subjects using disc reproduction a broken film is a more serious interruption than with ordinary subjects, on account of the need for synchronism between record and film, and with film reproduction, a break is also specially objectionable because it cuts off the music as well as the picture. Therefore, examine all synchronized films and sound films with extra care when rewinding, so as to catch tears before they develop into breaks. For this reason, rewind by hand and not by motor.

In film reproduction make especially sure that the film

has been put in as good condition as possible and that the mechanism is clean. Oil or grease from the projector or film pick-up mechanism is particularly liable to get on the first few feet of film.

Keep emergency films in containers unless they have to be used.

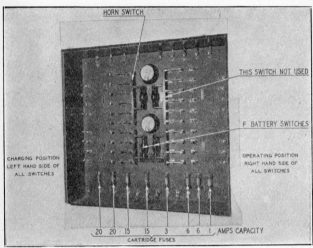

HORN SWITCH

THIS SWITCH NOT USED

F BATTERY SWITCHES

CHARGING POSITION
LEFT HAND SIDE OF
ALL SWITCHES

OPERATING POSITION
RIGHT HAND SIDE OF
ALL SWITCHES

20 20 15 15 3 6 6 1 AMPS CAPACITY
CARTRIDGE FUSES

Courtesy Western Electric Co.

FIG. 134

BATTERY PANEL 1-FD.

Synchronized films and sound films come treated ready for immediate use, and require no different care than ordinary films, except as just noted.

Keep all records in envelopes they come in, when not in use. Put each record in its envelope with the playing side next the felt, and facing you. Keep the records in correct order for the next show.

Synchronized Subjects. The process of running synchronized subjects, using either film or disc reproduction, is as follows:

Follow out starting and testing procedure, and set up first two synchronized numbers on the two machines to be used.

Strike arc on first projector in usual manner. When lamp is in operating condition and show is ready to proceed, start motor of first projector. When motor is up to speed open douser. Bring fader up slowly so that it reaches correct setting just before voice or music begins. (This needs rehearsal.)

Motor used in this equipment takes four or five seconds to speed up, because of heavy flywheel required. Never move fader from zero before motor has reached full speed, as this will completely spoil beginning of speech or music. If sound begins before motor has finished speeding up, add leader to film as required.

For sychronized feature pictures, keep track of operation by listening to monitor and by watching screen for cues. At cue "SM" as given on cue sheet, start motor on second machine. At cue "CO," operate change-over so as to switch picture from outgoing projector to incoming. As soon as voice or music from outgoing machine is finished, bring fader of this machine to zero and then up to proper setting for incoming machine in time to catch first note of music.

Stop outgoing machine, kill arc, and set up third film, and also third record, with disc method.

For synchronized subjects other than feature pictures, keep track of operation by listening to monitor and watching pictures. As soon as last note of music or last word is heard, bring fader to zero, then fade out picture as soon as subject matter requires. Start second machine in same manner as already described for first machine. Proper instant for starting second machine so as to get right time interval between end of first subject and beginning of second, must be determined by rehearsal.

Never stop motor on any machine before fader has been brought to zero or switched to incoming machine,

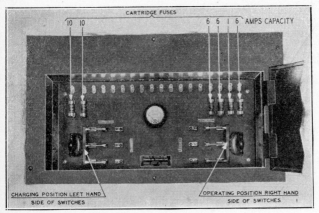

Courtesy Western Electric Co.

FIG. 135

BATTERY PANEL. 40 TYPE.

as otherwise end of speech or music will be spoiled. Stop outgoing machine, kill arc, and set up for third subject. Continue process of switching from one machine to the other until show is completed.

When synchronized presentations are finished shut down amplifier and power equipment. Put away films and records.

When using film pick-up, after running each reel

wipe off with a rag the light aperture and film tracks of aperture plate and tension pad in reproducing attachment, so as to guard against possibility of dirt accumulating and obstructing light beam or scratching film.

Non-Synchronized Subjects. When films without synchronized accompaniment are being used, and it is not desired to operate at the standard synchronized speed of 90 ft. per minute, throw the regulating switch on the motor control box to the "VAR" position and turn the control knob to regulate the speed as desired. The motor is started and stopped by the foot switch used in synchronized operation.

Use of Tilting Mechanism. If the house has both a front and back screen, change the projection angle, in going from one screen to the other, by turning the tilting handwheel. Upper and lower stop nuts are provided to check the movement of the handwheel when the correct angle is reached. Be sure to loosen the tilting clamp before turning the handwheel, and be sure to tighten it again when the angle has been changed.

If for any reason it is desired to change the tilt of the machine by a large amount, first see that the tilting clamp is tight, then loosen the two tilting stud setscrews which grip the tilting rod. Hold the rear of the lamp house bracket in one hand, loosen the tilting clamp with the other, and tilt the machine as desired. Then tighten clamp and setscrews.

Use of Foot Brake. When the foot switch is pressed down lightly, it turns off the starting switch and stops the machine. If it is pressed down more heavily, against the resistance of the spring, it applies a brake to the motor flywheel. However, this braking feature is not to be used as a regular thing, as this is not necessary and would cause excessive wear. It is only to be used in emergencies, such as film breakage, when a quick stop is necessary to avoid damage.

Rehearsing. In order to give a satisfactory performance with synchronized presentations, adequate rehearsal is necessary to cover the various points which will be listed.

The House Manager should be present at these re-

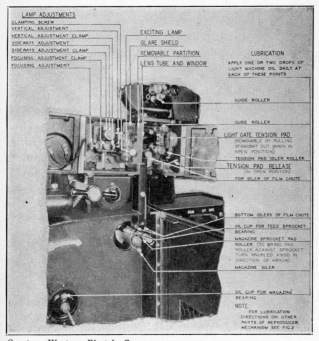

Courtesy Western Electric Co.

FIG. 136

FILM COMPARTMENTS SHOWING EXCITING LAMP.

hearsals with an observer at the telephone set. The subjects should be run off in the same way as for an actual performance. Time spent in careful rehearsing will be amply repaid in the perfection of the show, and the actual presence and interest of the House Manager is indispensable.

Light effects and any special features of the forthcoming show should be considered and tried out in conjunction with the rehearsal procedure described here.

Note that, as previously mentioned, adjustments in the timing of numbers must be confined to parts of the program other than the synchronized reels; the latter must always be run at standard speed, with the regulating switch on the motor control box set at "REG."

The points to check are as follows:

On first reel of each synchronized feature picture and on first of each group of short subjects shown, determine how soon after starting motor fader should be brought up to its full setting. It should be brought up slowly, taking two or three seconds, and should reach this point just before the voice or music begins. Add blank leader if necessary.

For remaining reels of a feature, determine how soon after change-over fader should be brought up to its full setting. Usually this will be immediately after change-over.

For short subjects, determine how soon after end of voice or music accompanying each subject the picture should be faded out.

On second and following subjects, determine when motor of incoming machine should be started to allow proper time interval between subjects, and when fader should be brought up to its setting to catch incoming music.

Courtesy Western Electric Co.

FIG. 137

REPRODUCER SET FOR FILM REPRODUCTION, SHOWING PROJECTOR
THREADED.

If using a safety device that stops motor when film has run through, see whether there are any reels where the film terminates before the end of the record is reached, and add blank film at end as required.

In houses where the upper horns are of the 12-A type and the lower horns of the 13-A type, and where an output control panel is used, with a separate control for each horn, three different types of combinations or settings of the upper and lower horns are used, and designated respectively by the letters "*A*", "*B*", and "*C*".

The "*A*" setting is for vocal and instrumental solos or speech and uses upper horns only or upper horns with some lower horn. The "*B*" setting adds more lower horn to bring out effect of orchestral accompaniment. The "*C*" setting is for orchestra alone and carries further result mentioned for the "*B*" setting.

As a matter of convenience, and in order to give the theatres the benefit of the opinion of the recording and engineering staffs, recommended fader and horn settings are frequently marked on records or films or given on cue sheets sent out with them. Electrical Research engineers so adjust the amplifiers that with a full house, and fader setting recommended, correct full house volume is obtained. With house only partially filled fader should be brought down one or two steps.

Determine horn settings and empty house fader setting for each number, bearing in mind any recommendations marked on or accompanying record or film. Do this with care and in particular do not permit too high a volume. Synchronized scores to feature pictures should be run at a volume appropriate to incidental music. Never make the volume so loud that it causes the needles to oscillate on the amplifier plate current

meters. If this happens it is a pure sign of overloading
and poor quality.

Speakers talking at a distance or in conversational
tones should be reproduced with less volume than those
speaking close or obviously talking loudly. Instrumen-

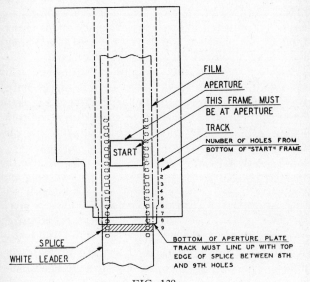

FILM

APERTURE

THIS FRAME MUST
BE AT APERTURE

TRACK

NUMBER OF HOLES FROM
BOTTOM OF "START" FRAME

START

1
2
3
4
5
6
7
8
9

SPLICE

WHITE LEADER

BOTTOM OF APERTURE PLATE
TRACK MUST LINE UP WITH TOP
EDGE OF SPLICE BETWEEN 8TH
AND 9TH HOLES

FIG. 138

SETTING FILM FOR DISC REPRODUCTION.

tal solos should have less volume than full orchestras
(not accompanying), bands, etc. In news reels, street
noises, locomotive whistles, etc., should be loud to give
correct illusion. In certain records effect may be improved by bringing fader up or down a step at certain
points in the picture, as just mentioned. Even the horn

settings may occasionally be changed during a number as record changes from light or vocal effects, which are best reproduced by upper horns, to heavier orchestra music for which lower horns are brought out. However, discretion must be used in not making too great or too frequent changes in horn and fader settings; each record is made under skilled musical and technical direction in such a manner that when it is reproduced the effect desired by composer, artist, and conductor will be obtained without any need for frequently changing settings while playing. If they are changed too much, therefore, proper effect will not be obtained.

Troubles. If this equipment is properly maintained it should rarely give trouble in operation.

All the information given here has been carefully prepared on the basis of operating experience gained with large numbers of theatres. The operator should make himself familiar with it so that he can quickly locate and remedy troubles, and continue a program with the minimum of interruption if trouble arises during a show.

Remember that whenever the sound is not coming over as it should, the fader can be employed to cut it out until the trouble has been located and remedied. It is much better to do this than to continue the sound accompaniment when it is obviously bad. If the fader is properly handled all kinds of trouble may happen and be remedied by the projectionist without the audience noticing anything seriously amiss.

Whenever trouble occurs, use the emergency equipment or emergency set-up if one is provided, and endeavor to locate and remedy the difficulty, if possible, by following the instructions given here. If you are unable to do so, notify the Electrical Research engineer. Do not attempt extensive repair or replacement work on the equipment, as this usually requires expert knowledge.

When one of the fuses burns out, replace it by a new fuse of the same type, as covered in the instructions which follow, but if it blows a second time, do not renew it until the cause of the trouble has been found and remedied.

Before removing the rear cover of any piece of amplifier equipment, be sure to turn off the power and keep it off till the cover is replaced. Also switch off the power on the battery switching and charging panel before replacing any fuses.

If all conditions appear normal, and still no sound is heard from the horns, and no relief is afforded by any of the procedures that will be described, the indications are that a break or short circuit exists somewhere in the sound circuit. In this case listen in with the headset along this circuit, starting at the disc or film pick-up with a record playing, and working on towards the horns until the location of the fault is shown by coming to a spot beyond which nothing is heard. Be sure to use very little gain, as otherwise the headset will be overloaded and possibly damaged, and the quality will be spoiled. Use the same method to locate the source of noise or bad quality.

Use a battery and buzzer to test lines for opens or shorts, but never to test amplifier or reproducer circuits, as this may upset the magnetic characteristics of the coils.

On some amplifiers two or more tubes are operated with their filaments in series; if one tube burns out, the others will then be extinguished. If two or more tubes go dark at once, therefore, it should be realized that only one has burnt out. This tube may be located by inspection, or the replacing tube can be tried in each socket in turn.

Charger Not Functioning (AC Supply Only). On charger used with AC supply, if a rectifier bulb does not light, its filament may be burned out. Also, a fuse on battery panel may have blown. Clean tube socket. If tube still does not light, replace it by one of spares supplied. If tubes light but charger does not give output, a fuse inside charger may have blown.

Motor Does Not Start. Is line switch on? Fuse may have blown in motor control box.

Reading on Motor Control Box Meter Not Within Specified Limits. If reading is too high, on AC, or too low, on DC, it indicates excessive friction at some point in mechanism. If this is not attended to immediately a bearing may freeze, rendering a projector temporarily useless. Stop machine and oil all bearings immediately abnormal reading is noted on meter, particularly any bearing that seems unduly hot. If trouble persists, notify service man.

Motor Does Not Maintain Regulated Speed. Notify service engineer.

Unsteady Pitch in Reproducing ("Flutter"). With film reproduction, there may be dirt on the sprocket in the film compartment of the attachment. If this cause does not exist, notify service engineer.

Reproducer Not Tracking Properly. This occurs when needle jumps from groove. See that reproducer is not dragging on record and that it is not hitting anything or otherwise being hindered from free movement.

Put in new needle. Try new record. The swivel base on which the reproducer swings is mounted on a bracket, which in turn is clamped to the base by a bolt. See that the bracket is level and that the bolt has not loosened and allowed it to turn.

Courtesy Western Electric Co.

FIG. 139

SETTING REPRODUCER AT STARTING POINT ON RECORD.

Excessive or Insufficient Plate Current. If this is noticed on testing the amplifiers, replace the tube showing this condition by a spare.   When two or more tubes on an amplifier all show low plate current at the same time, try replacing the rectifier tubes on that amplifier (the 41-A amplifier uses the rectifier tubes on the 42-A amplifier). This may also be a sign of defective condensers.

No Sound From One Horn. Fuse may have blown in cutout box back-stage. If fuse in cutout box has not blown, replace receiver.

Volume Falls Off or Ceases. If system is a double one, having emergency amplifier equipment, put in emergency amplifiers by means of key on system transfer panel. If this clears trouble, continue use of emergency amplifiers until service engineer repairs or replaces defective regular amplifier, unless trouble can be cleared. One of amplifier tubes may be burnt out. If so, replace with a new tube of same type.

One horn may have short in line or winding through which sound current passes, thereby causing others to receive no power. Turn off all horns by means of keys on output control panel, or if these are not provided, then by means of switches in horn cutout box backstage, and then try to locate bad receiver by turning horns on and off one at a time. They should all give volume except bad one. If defective receiver is found, replace by spare.

Possibly fuses in horn supply circuit on battery panel have blown. Check reproducers by switching from one to the other on fader. If one is bad, replace. If neither gives any sound, check fader and circuit by means of headset, or as follows:

In systems using 41, 42 and 43 type amplifiers, left-hand key at top of fader, called fader cutout key can be used to cut out either side of fader circuit. If this key is thrown to left, (red) for example, reproducing equipment on "red" machine will be connected direct to amplifiers without going through "red" side of fader.

Similarly when key is thrown to right (white) side, "white" machine is connected direct to amplifiers. To check whether trouble is due to defect in fader, try using cutout key in this manner. If this eliminates trouble, use cutout key for change-overs, instead of

Courtesy Western Electric Co.

FIG. 140

CONNECTIONS AND CORRECT POSITION FOR PHOTO-ELECTRIC CELL.

fader, until service engineer can repair or replace latter. Regulate volume by means of gain control on 41-A amplifier.

With film reproduction, exciting lamp may be out of focus or burnt out, or opening in photo-electric cell may be out of line with opening leading to film compartment. Position cell properly.

If system uses one or more 43 type amplifiers, and plate current reading on one of these amplifiers is very low or is zero, probably a condenser has failed. A further indication of this is that plates of rectifier tubes of amplifier affected may begin to get red hot. Turn off power on this amplifier, by means of amplifier starting switch. Locate defective condenser as follows:

Remove front cover or amplifier. The condensers are connected in parallel in two groups, the first group containing C-2 to C-10 inclusive and the second group C-11 to C-19 inclusive. Unsolder connection coming from behind panel to lower terminal of C-2. Turn amplifier starting switch to "Plate." If plate meter reading is now normal, it shows bad condenser is in C-2 to C-10 group. Shut off switch. Restore connection on C-2, and unsolder connection between C-2 and C-3. Turn on switch. If meter reading is still normal, it shows C-2 is good and bad condenser is in C-3 to C-10 group. Restore connection on C-3 and unsolder connection between C-3 and C-4; test again with switch and meter, and so on until a condenser is found which when connected causes meter reading to fall. This will be the bad condenser. Cut it out by connecting together directly the lower terminals of the two adjoining condensers, instead of making the connection through the lower terminal of the defective condenser.

If in the first place, when the connection coming from

behind the panel is unsoldered from the lower terminal of C-2, this does not bring the meter reading back to normal, it shows that the defective condenser is in the C-11 to C-19 group. Then restore connection on C-2, unsolder connection between C-11 and C-12, and test for defective condenser as already described for C-2 to C-10 group.

If all fuses are in good condition and all current and voltage readings normal, probably there is a ground, open circuit or short circuit somewhere in the system. Try to locate fault with headset. Possibly a loose or grounded connection may be found, which can easily be repaired.

If system has no emergency amplifiers and includes one 43-A amplifier, and this is found to be defective, disconnect its "Input" and "Output" terminals (accessible by removing the back cover) and run system off 500 ohm "Output" terminals of 42-A amplifier. If system uses two 43-A amplifiers and one is found to be defective disconnect its "Input" and "Output" terminals. When cutting out an amplifier as just described the loss of power can be partly compensated for by running the fader higher, or raising the gain control dial on the 41-A amplifier one or two steps. Be careful not to impair quality by raising fader or gain so much as to overload amplifiers.

Poor Quality or Noisy Output. See paragraph under previous heading "Volume Falls Off or Ceases."

One of amplifier or rectifier tubes may be burnt out. Replace with spare of same type. For amplifier use, this must be a new tube. A receiver may be defective. Test horns one by one. Film may be scratched or dirty.

A reproducer may be defective. Fader may be defective.

One of amplifier tubes may be defective. Take a new tube and try it in place of each tube in turn until the noisy one is located.

Storage batteries may be dirty on top. See that they are kept clean.

Storage batteries may have been put in use too soon

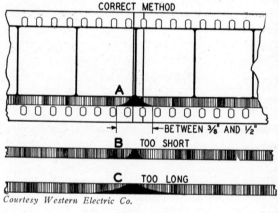

CORRECT METHOD

A

←BETWEEN ⅜" AND ½"

B TOO SHORT

C TOO LONG

Courtesy Western Electric Co.

FIG. 142

SPLICING SOUND FILM.

after charging, while still gassing. About half an hour is required for gassing to cease completely. Storage battery connections may be loose. Keep them tight.

There may be poor ground or loose connection at some point in system. Examine connections and tighten any found loose. If trouble still unsolved, use headset, and if a defective 43-A amplifier is found, cut it out.

Observer's Equipment Not Functioning. If not loud enough to enable observer and operator to hear each other, or if buzzer is weak or inoperative, make sure that switch on box is pulled out, and that batteries are in good condition. Replace batteries (open battery box by loosening screw in cover). If trouble not here, check line for shorts or opens.

Troubles Occurring During Show.—Film Breaks (Film Reproduction). As synchronism between pictures and sound is inherent in the film, no loss of synchronism is occasioned by a break. Therefore, deal with a broken sound film the same as with an ordinary film in the same circumstances.

Film Breaks (Disc Reproduction). Douse light, turn fader to zero, and stop motor. The next step, as specified below, will depend on whether the break is above the intermittent or below it, and whether the sound only consists of a musical accompaniment and incidental effects, or whether there is speech, close-ups, etc., which make synchronism very important.

Break Below Intermittent—All Cases. Run down film needed for winding around take-up, by means of handwheel. Do not disturb film at aperture plate, or record and reproducer. Continue run, bringing fader to regular setting as soon as full speed is reached.

Synchronism will usually be maintained under these conditions. However, since audience will lose some of the subject, it is generally better in the case of short subjects not to wait for restarting as just described, but to continue performance immediately by showing next subject, which is set up on other machine. In meantime broken film can be repaired and shown again at con-

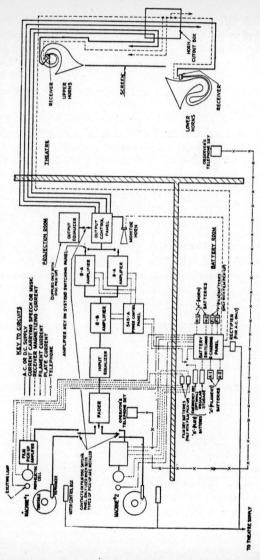

GENERAL LAYOUT "2 SX" EQUIPMENT

clusion of number which is running on other machine. If break was near end of reel it may not be worth while returning to subject.

Break Above Intermittent.—With Speech or Other Sound Accompaniment Where Exact Synchronism is Essential. In this case it is not possible to continue on broken film without losing synchronism, and there is therefore no option except to continue program with next reel, which is set up on other machine, or else cut out sound for remainder of this reel.

Break Above Intermittent.—With Speech or Other Sound Accompaniment Where Exact Synchronism is Not Essential. Rethread and continue as previously described for break below intermittent. Synchronism is usually lost under these conditions, but this can be tolerated in an emergency, unless there is a direct cue in record, such as a knock, voice or cheers. In such a case, pass over cue with fader on zero.

Needle Jumps Groove. If the needle jumps back the sound will repeat, and may keep on repeating at every revolution of the record. If the needle jumps forward, the sound will be ahead of the picture. The procedure will depend on the character of the film and on where the jump occurs. Any record on which the needle has jumped must never be used again, and the reproducer should be checked as soon as possible. Bring fader to zero immediately jump is noticed; the next procedure will depend on circumstances, as follows:

With Speech or Other Sound Accompaniment Where Exact Synchronism is Essential. In this case it is not possible to continue without losing synchronism, and there is therefore no option except to continue program with next reel, which is set up on other machine, or else cut out sound for remainder of this reel.

With Music or Other Sound Accompaniment, Where Exact Synchronism is Not Essential. Keep projector running, and look over reproducer quickly to see if

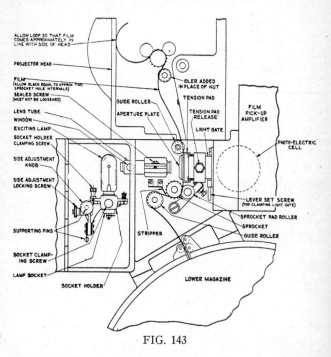

FIG. 143

there is any visible cause for jump, such as reproducer body dragging on record, or reproducer hitting something that prevents it from moving freely. If so, remove obstacle or change reproducer. This, of course,

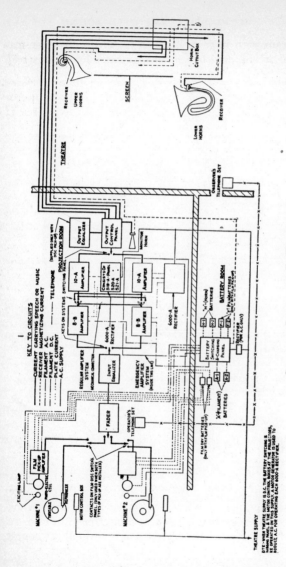

GENERAL LAYOUT 1-D EQUIPMENT

involves loss of acompaniment for remainder of reel. If no cause for trouble is evident, then, if needle jumped back, change needle, move reproducer over to a position two or three grooves ahead of where it was when it jumped, and restore fader to its regular setting. If needle jumped forward, and if it now seems to be tracking properly, restore fader to regular setting.

Synchronism is lost when record is continued after needle has jumped, so in such cases if there are any direct cues in picture, such as knocks, voices, cheers, etc., fader must be put down to zero when passing over them.

Replacements. While projectionists are expected to follow the instructions previously given for dealing with equipment troubles and to do simple repair work on the apparatus, such as soldering broken connections, replacing burnt out tubes or burnt out fuses, tightening loose parts, replacing defective parts by other parts supplied or recommended for the purpose, they must never experiment with the equipment by changing circuits or substituting coils, condensers, etc., of other types, or by using records of types not authorized, as this might result in a situation constituting default of contract with the theatre.

Keep all spare parts in a clean, dry place; be sure that the temperature is not above 80°, as this causes deterioration of the photo-electric cells.

Changing Receivers. If a defective receiver is found by application of the various tests described in these instructions, replace it by one of the spares furnished. Be sure to connect each wire to the same terminal on the new receiver as it was connected to on the old one. All four receiver terminals are marked for this purpose.

If a receiver is connected wrongly, the quality of the sound as heard in the house will be spoilt.

Never open receivers or attempt to repair them. Never operate a receiver without the horn, as this may damage it.

In installations having only one horn, if this horn is provided with a receiver switching device the spare receiver may be put in use by simply moving over the throat lever. The double-throw switch located in the stage cutout box, which controls the sound circuit to the receivers, must also be thrown to the other position so as to connect in the spare receiver.

Changing Reproducers. If a defective reproducer is found by application of the various tests described in these instructions, replace it by one of the spares furnished.

The base of the reproducer assembly (swivel, arm and reproducer unit) fits on a bracket attached to the turntable pedestal. This base is clamped to the bracket by means of a milled thumbscrew. When this thumbscrew is loosened and the output leads disconnected from the connecting block, the whole reproducer assembly can be removed. The simplicity of this operation makes it the best method of changing reproducers quickly.

To change a 4-A reproducer unit, remove the two screws attaching the unit to the arm; you will see one of these screws at each side of the reproducer just behind the head. This leaves the unit loose except for the output leads; turn it over on its back, thereby exposing the terminal block and remove the leads by loosening the binding screws that attach them to the

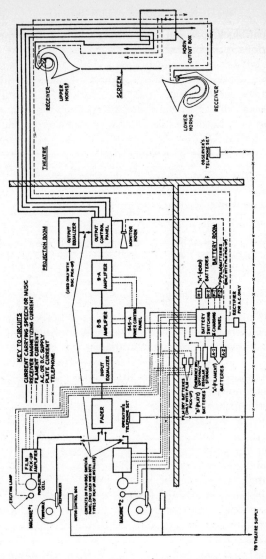

GENERAL LAYOUT 2S EQUIPMENT

terminal block. To put in a new 4-A unit, follow these operations in reverse order.

On no account open a 4-A reproducer unit or loosen any screws other than those mentioned, as it is filled with a special damping compound and will be ruined if this leaks out. Never attempt to repair or adjust reproducers. Before using a new reproducer during a show, test it by playing a record with it or listening across its terminals with the headset.

Changing Photo-Electric Cells. Be sure to see that the window in the cell lining is properly lined up with the opening in the partition separating the cell compartment and the film compartment.

Splicing Film—Disc Reproduction. Vitaphone film has 16 frames per foot, and each foot is numbered. Beginning with "O" at the starting mark, the 16th frame after the starting mark is marked No. 1. The 16th frame after No. 1 is marked No. 2, and so on throughout the print. There are, therefore 15 frames without numbers between each pair of numbers. By this system, the position of every single frame in the reel is indicated. In synchronized features there are in addition other numbers on the margin of the film which indicate the scene numbers of the picture. These numbers can be distinguished from the footage numbers, because they have a dash at each side, as for instance "—286—", the footage numbers themselves being simply "286," without the dash at either end. In cases where the scene and footage numbers conflict, the footage number is omitted, but is counted, and reference will have to be made to the next footage number in sequence.

If a footage number does not appear at each 16th frame, continue counting until you reach the next number, when you should then have 31 frames between the two footage numbers.

With the numbering system described, it is easy to ascertain whether or not a print has the proper number of frames, by simply examing each splice and counting the footage numbers on each side. The two numbers should be consecutive and there should be 15 frames without numbers between them.

In case of a break in a film, make a patch by inserting black leader. Be sure that the number of frames of black leader inserted is exactly the same as the number of frames you take out of the film, plus the frames used for the patches. After putting in the black leader, be sure to check up and see that the numbers follow in sequence and that there are exactly 15 frames without numbers between each pair of footage numbers.

If any numbered frames are missing, or if the missing portion is more than one foot, you will have to check both sides of the break to the next number, and after making the splice, see that you do not forget the intervening numbered frames.

Splicing Film—Film Reproduction. In case film carrying a sound track becomes broken, cut out as few frames as possible when making the splice. A break in the sound track is usually even more noticeable to the audience than a break in the picture. However, do not go to the extreme of saving weak film that will cause trouble later.

A plain splice, no matter how carefully made, will cause a click to be heard from the sound projectors as it passes through the film reproducing attachment, because the two edges and the overlap disturb the uniformity of the sound track and produce the same effect as though noises had actually been recorded on the track. In dealing with film of this type, therefore, first make a splice in the usual manner and then paint over this splice in place, as shown at "*A*" in Fig. 142. The painted mark on the sound track should be roughly triangular in shape with a blunted apex and between ⅜" and ½" wide at the base. If the splice is painted in this manner it will be almost inaudible when passing through the reproducing attachment, as the change in the light intensity which it causes will be at a frequency below the audible range. If the mark is made too short, as shown in figure "*B*", the click will be very pronounced; if it is made too long, as in figure "*C*", there will not be a click but there will be a noticeable pause in the sound owing to so much of the sound track being obliterated.

For opaqueing splices, the use of Zapon Concentrated Black Lacquer No. 2,002-2 is recommended. It is made by the Zapon Company, Stamford, Connecticut. When a thinner is necessary, Zapon thinner No. 20 is recommended. The lacquer should be applied to the shiny, or celluloid, side of the film and not to the emulsion side. It dries almost instantly, adheres tightly, and is much more satisfactory than India ink or other substances. If for any reason it should become necessary to remove it, a rag soaked in lacquer thinner will be effective.

Splices in the negative in making up subjects sent out by the producers are taken care of in the printing and may be observed by the triangular marks along the sound track near changes of scene.

Courtesy Samson Electric Co.

FIG. 145

SAMSON ELECTRIC AMPLIFIER.

SAMSON RECORDING AMPLIFIER

THE photograph Fig. 145 is of a complete recording amplifier built by the Samson Electric Company.

In addition to being a recording amplifier, it can be used with practically no changes as a Group Address amplifier as well. It is entirely DC-operated, and is not intended for operation from "B" eliminators or with AC tubes.

The top panel is a four-microphone mixing panel, and the row of 12 binding posts across the top is for the input leads from four microphones. The four switches are for turning on or off each individual microphone and associated vacuum tubes. The knobs underneath these binding posts are the volume control for each individual microphone. The second series of knobs are microphone rheostats for controlling the button current for each one of these microphones, and the jacks underneath these last knobs are for reading the individual button current of the four microphones; the current showing on the Weston milliammeter in the centre of the microphone mixing panel.

The next panel below is the amplifier panel. The first meter on the upper left of this panel is for reading in connection with the plug and jack on the lower portion of this same panel, the plate currents in the mixer panel, and in the first, second and third stage of the main amplifier. The central meter is for reading the last stage left power tube plate current, and is in circuit at all times. The right hand upper meter is for reading the last stage right hand power tube plate current, and is in circuit at all times. The left hand lower meter in this panel is for reading the battery voltage of approximately 12 volts. The right hand lower meter is a volume indicator meter, and can be put in or out of the circuit by throwing the switch marked "volume indicator" directly below it. The two knobs in the centre are volume controls, the left hand one being that of the main amplifier, and the right hand one being that controlling the volume indicator. The central lower knob is for setting the volume indicator; in other words, without any signal coming through from the microphone, you adjust this lower central knob until the amplifier reads slightly above zero. The switch directly below it marked "high" and "low" covers the gain in the amplifier; in other words, if you bring up (with the switch set at "low") the knob marked "amplifier gain" and you do not obtain enough volume, you return the amplifier gain knob to zero, and throw the switch to "high" and you are at exactly the same point in volume as you were with the switch at "low" and the amplifier gain in maximum. Then you come up on your amplifier gain again to its maximum volume. The left hand switch is more or less self-explanatory, being a switch for turning off and on the "A" battery and the "B" batteries. The right hand switch is also self-explanatory, turning off and on the main amplifier or turning on and off the volume indicator.

The last panel is particularly applicable to the requirements for which the amplifier was built. The left hand meter and knob controlling the current for the light which is located in the camera for recording sound on the film, and the right hand meter and knob in this panel are for another light located in another camera. The switch in the centre is self-explanatory. The left hand switch turns on or off the camera No. 1, and the

right hand switch turning on or off camera No. 2. The
middle switch is for turning on or off a monitor speaker
located near the operator. The lowest panel is for the
connection of various wires to the amplifier.

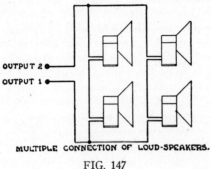

MULTIPLE CONNECTION OF LOUD-SPEAKERS.

FIG. 147

INSTRUCTIONS FOR USE OF PAM AMPLIFIERS

PAMS 16, 17, and 18 are two-stage AC operated audio amplifiers having an undistorted output of approximately seven watts. Power to operate the tubes is obtained from a 105-120-volt 50-60-cycle source. Pam 16 employs a 227 tube in the first-stage and push-pull 210's in the second, while Pam 17 is similar, with a 165-volt supply for the field of one dynamic speaker requiring 110-220 volts DC for excitation. Pam 18 is similar to Pam 17, with a 226 tube in the first stage instead of the 227. The input binding posts are connected directly to the primary of an audio transformer having an impedance of 25,000 ohms at 100 cycles with no DC in the winding. The amplifier terminates in an output transformer designed to work into an impedance of 2,000 ohms at 100 cycles. This is suitable for the average magnetic or dynamic speaker incorporating its own transformer as found on the market. These amplifiers are capable of handling fifteen of the more efficient loud-speakers at sufficient volume so that each producer will fill an average room. An overall gain of approximately 45 T.U. is obtained. None of these amplifiers supply power to a radio set or any tubes external to the amplifier, the field of a speaker being the only external load fed from the power supply. It is not feasible to use the field voltage for the "B" supply of a radio set.

Pams 19 and 20 are three-stage AC operated audio amplifiers similar to the smaller Pams with the following differences. The input impedance is approximately

100,000 ohms at 100 cycles with no DC in the windings. These amplifiers have an undistorted output of approximately fifteen watts, making them capable of handling twice as many speakers, i.e., thirty, at sufficient volume so that each reproducer will fill an average room. An overall gain of approximately 60 T.U. is obtained. 227 tubes are used in the first two stages and push-pull 250's in the last stage. Pam 20 is similar to Pam 19 with the addition of the supply for the field of one dynamic speaker. Due to the power obtainable from these amplifiers, there should be more than one speaker connected to the output if damage to a single speaker is to be avoided. Even the larger type of dynamic speakers is apt to rattle when fed the entire power from Pam 19 or Pam 20. Of course, a number of smaller speakers can be used to advantage by employing a series-parallel connection.

When any type Pam is to be used for group address work, it will be necessary to precede it by a two-stage amplifier and the necessary equipment to supply button current to the microphone. A standard two-button microphone cannot be used directly with a Pam. The Samson Mik-1 is an all AC microphone input and two-stage amplifier designed to work into any Pam, giving a complete group address system employing no batteries.

The Pam should be mounted on a flat surface so that the tubes will be in a vertical position. If the amplifier is to be transported or shipped after installation, it should be secured in place by at least four 10-32 steel machine screws or their equivalent. In choosing a location for the Pam, especially when confined, see that some provision is made for ventilation. Under normal conditions from fifty to sixty watts of heat are generated by the tubes and amplifier, necessitating free circulation of air within a cabinet or console.

After the Pam has been fastened in place, the connections are made as in Fig. 146. When used for record reproduction, the cord from the electrical pick-up connects directly to the two binding posts marked "Input." If no volume control or scratch filter is furnished with the pick-up, they may be inserted as shown in the diagram. A 20,000-ohm potentiometer connected across the input makes a very suitable volume control for this type of amplifier. The Samson Electric Company manufactures a scratch filter which helps to reduce the unpleasant needle noise found with phonograph reproduction. Remember, however, that removing the scratch also takes out some of the high notes, since both lie in the same region. Some of the pick-ups found on the market today already have a similar scratch filter incorporated within the volume control. It is often advisable to ground the low side of the pick-up circuit (Input 2), especially when long leads are used. This connection is shown by a dotted line in Fig. 146.

The diagram shows the connections of a Pam amplifier to a rado set. "Input 1" being the high side of the amplifier should always be connected to the plate of the detector tube. Do not attempt to operate the Pam from the first audio stage or the entire output of a radio set, since the first stage in the Pam will probably be overloaded, causing distortion; also, a poor audio transformer in the radio set will render useless the superior quality of the Pam. It is advisable to leave the tubes in the audio stages of AC sets, although they are not used, when using a Pam amplifier, in order that the voltages on the remaining tubes of the set will remain at their rated value. This is particularly true of the filament circuit, where excessive voltage materially shortens the life of tubes.

The speaker is connected to the two binding posts marked "Output." In the case of Pam 17, 18, or 20, the field of the speaker should be connected to the posts marked "Field," but only to such dynamic speakers as specify for field supply 90 to 220 volts DC. In some cases where hum is introduced in the speaker it may be reduced somewhat by reversing the field connections to the amplifier. If no field connection is to be used on the above types of amplifier, a 2,500-ohm, 5-watt resistor must be connected across the field binding posts. Failure to connect a load on the field binding post will place undue strain on the resistor or condensers inside the amplifier.

When more than one speaker is to be employed, the connections should be such as to make the impedance of the combination appear as near to that of a single speaker as possible. Fig. 147 shows the arrangement for four dynamic speakers. It must be remembered that Pams 17, 18, and 20 supply field current for only one dynamic speaker. When more than one speaker is employed, or where a Pam other than Pam 17, 18, or 20 is used, it will be necessary to obtain the field excitation from some external source.

After carefully checking all connections, the tubes should be placed in their proper sockets and the primary plug connected to the power block. Set the number corresponding most nearly to the line voltage uppermost. If the line voltage is not known, set the plug for 120, reducing it a step at a time if proper operation is not obtained. If no difference is noted, operate the amplifier with 120 on top, since in this position, the

voltages in the amplifier are lowest and increased tube
life results. The switch in the cord may be used to
turn the amplifier on or off.

With the volume control shut off, or set for lowest
volume, start the radio set or phonograph in the usual
manner. Gradually increase the volume until satisfactory results are obtained.

Care should be taken to see that the AC line is disconnected while working on the amplifier. Disagree-
able and dangerous shocks may be obtained from the
output or field leads due to the high voltages developed
in the amplifier.

Do not attempt to operate the amplifier with the
speaker disconnected. Without proper load on the
output stage, abnormally high voltages will be developed, possibly causing damage to the output transformer.

Sufficient ventilation should be provided to allow
dissipation of the heat generated by the tubes and
resistor in the amplifier.

Always use a resistor (2,500 ohms, 5 watts) across
the field binding posts of Pams 17, 18, and 20 when no
field current is to be taken from the amplifier. Failure
to do this places an undue strain on the resistor or condensers inside the Pam.

Use only the specified size of fuse. Pams 16, 17,
and 18 take a three-ampere fuse, while Pams 19 and
20 take one of six amperes rating. Fuses are inserted
in the circuit. If a fuse blows, look for trouble!

Do not remove the 210 or 250 tubes from their
sockets while the amplifier is in operation. Without
the load of these tubes the voltage of the power supply
reaches a very high value, placing a severe strain on the
filter condensers.

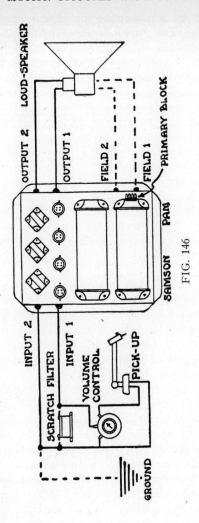

FIG. 146

Probably the most common trouble arising with the use of a Pam is the presence of an AC hum. A simple test to determine whether or not the hum originates in the amplifier may be made by connecting the two input binding posts together while the amplifier is in operation. There should be no appreciable sound coming from the loud-speaker. More hum is to be expected in the Pam 19 or 20 due to the addition of a third stage, and in the Pam 18 due to the use of a 226 tube. However, with the extra volume available in the larger Pam, the ratio of output to hum should be about the same as in the small Pam.

When using the Pam in conjunction with a radio set employing the 226 type of tube, a fairly pronounced hum often will be found when the set is tuned to a station. This is caused by the hum in the radio set affecting the incoming signal, and is not due to the Pam amplifier.

Should a slight hum or rattle develop in the power block or one of the small audio transformers of the amplifier, it will not affect the operation of the Pam, since it cannot be heard in the loud-speaker. This hum is caused by the vibration of laminations. If hum is picked up by the leads to the input circuit, the best remedy is to shield the high lead (connecting to Input 1) with a metal covering such as copper braid or armored cable (BX), grounding the shield.

Failure of the amplifier to function may be investigated by touching the metal part of Input 1 binding post, which causes, under normal conditions, a distinct hum to be heard. If the tubes fail to light, look for a blown fuse or open switch in the power circuit. Little or no volume may be caused by failure to connect the field of the loud-speaker or to use an external resistor across the field binding posts when no field current is needed, or by insufficient input voltage to the amplifier.

Another very common source of trouble is poor tubes. Low volume, a scratching noise, or fading may be caused by a defective 227. The amplifier should continue to work with one 210 or 250 tube removed, though the power output is thereby greatly reduced. This practice is not recommended because it not only overloads the filter condensers but destroys the proper relations for the best quality of reproduction.

A high whistle or overloading at low volume suggest oscillation in the amplifier. This is usually caused by the input leads crossing or coming too close to the output leads. If it is absolutely necessary that they run together, one or both should be shielded. Grounding the base of the Pam will often help in a case of instability.

INSTRUCTIONS FOR S-M 678PD
PHONOGRAPH AMPLIFIER

THE Silver-Marshall 678PD Phonograph Amplifier is intended to take its input either from a phonograph with any suitable magnetic pick-up, or from the detector tube of a broadcast or short wave receiving set, amplifying such input about 450 times to a maximum of approximately 4,500 milliwatts—sufficient to fill any moderate size theatre of 1,000 to 2,000 seats.

Three tubes are required: one UX281 (CX381) rectifier tube, one UX226 (CX326) amplifying tube, and one UX250 (CX350) power amplifying tube.

The 678PD amplifier supplies field excitation current for the dynamic speaker with which it is used. The speaker should be of the type having field coil wound for approximately 110 volts DC. One or more additional speakers, located at other points in a hall, can also be connected to the 678PD amplifier, but a separate source of field current must be provided, preferably as a self-contained rectifier, as in "AC" types of dynamic speakers. Magnetic speakers may be used if lugs 3 and 4 of an S-M 331 or 331-U Unichoke are connected to the field coil posts of the 678PD. Fig. 150 shows the S-M amplifier in case.

To operate the 678PD amplifier, insert the three tubes as follows: '50 type nearest to the front panel; '26 type in middle socket; and '81 type in rear socket. To amplify a phonograph pick-up, connect the leads from the pick-up or its volume control to the two posts marked P and GND. Connect the input leads of the dynamic speaker to the two posts marked SPEAKER.

Connect the speaker field coil leads to the two posts marked TO CHOKE OR FIELD. If input is taken from a radio receiver instead of from the phonograph pick-up, connect GND to the negative side of the A battery or A power supply on the receiver; P to the P post of the detector socket in the receiver; B+ to the detector post of receiver B power unit, or to detector voltage terminal of B battery.

Courtesy Silver Marshall, Inc.

FIG. 150

S. M. AMPLIFIER.

Caution. Only when above connections have been carefully made and checked over, insert the plug at end of cord in a wall socket or other fixture supplying 105 to 120 volt, 50 to 60 cycle AC. Do not plug in on AC supply until all tubes are in place and all four leads connected to speaker. This provides the proper operating load for the filter and prevents possible condenser damage.

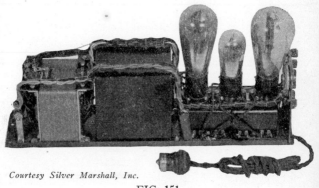

Courtesy Silver Marshall, Inc.

FIG. 151

S. M. Phonograph Amplifier with Cover Removed.

If receiver or phonograph is operating, speaker should reproduce at good volume. With a screwdriver adjust the "hum balance" on panel of the 678PD amplifier to the point of minimum hum.

When full output is not required, volume can be reduced by the volume control supplied with the phonograph pick-up, or by the volume control on the radio receiver. If the volume control on the receiver does not control the output of the 678PD amplifier, a 3,000 ohm potentiometer, connected as a rheostat between antenna and ground leads of the receiver, will serve. Fig. 151 shows the amplifier with cover removed.

The 678PD amplifier can be mounted in a cabinet, if desired, but care must be taken to provide for ample ventilation and air circulation to prevent overheating. If installation is properly made, as above described, the amplifier should require no further attention during the life of the tubes used.

Courtesy Silver Marshall, Inc.

FIG. 154

REAR VIEW OF S. M. UNIPAC.

S-M RACK-AND-PANEL "PA" AMPLIFIERS

THE Public Address Amplifiers now offered by Silver-Marshall, Inc., are so variegated in capabilities and form that any desired type of system for any class of service may be easily assembled from the unit panels which form their basis. With these new Silver-Marshall "P. A." type panels fully light socket operated amplifiers can be had to serve the smallest theatre or the largest auditorium. It was in the interest of low cost for what must always remain individually engineered installations, and great initial and operational flexibility, that the unit idea of assembly was adopted. The availability of S-M units should inspire more uses for quality amplification than ever before.

Figs. 152-153 show a popular type of high-grade P. A. amplifier system made up from the S-M unit panel assemblies mounted in a standard steel rack. Its undistorted power output is about thirty watts, and the overall amplification sufficient to give adequate volume for any use to which it may be put. With suitable loudspeakers, it will give voice, phonograph music, or radio coverage of a theatre of 6,000 seats or more.

A description of the different units making up this system will indicate their flexibility. The system illustrated consists of a steel rack carrying, from top to bottom, a visual volume indicator panel, an input control (selector) panel, an input amplifier panel, a test meter panel, an input amplifier power supply panel, two push-pull output power amplifier panels, and two blank panels for loud-speaker control, or other apparatus. All operating power is drawn from any 105 to 120 volt, 50 to 60 cycle, alternating current lighting circuit (except for eight dry cells for microphone operation). Through the use of a rotary converter, the system can be operated from any available power lines.

The type PA-1A AMPLIFIER RACK, or framework, is standard for mounting of all systems and is clearly depicted in all photographs. The side beams are heavy steel channels connected at the top by two steel straps and at the bottom by steel angle feet extending sufficiently to support the complete assembly. For permanent installation the feet should be bolted to the floor through holes provided. The rack assembly is effected by nuts and bolts; it can be easily and quickly assembled. PA-1A AMPLIFIER RACKS are finished in black crystal lacquer and racks are equipped with an "ON-OFF" switch in the upper cross-bar which, connected to all power panels, controls the whole system.

All panel sizes and piercings are co-ordinated with rack size and piercing in such manner that any Silver-Marshall P. A. panels can be inserted in any position in the rack. Panels can be replaced or interchanged to meet new conditions with little mechanical work.

Standard aluminum panels are of two sizes: 8″x21″ x¼″ and 4″x21″x¼″. The large panels are equipped with dust covers of heavy gauge aluminum which provide effective electrical shielding for the units as well. These covers slip over four corner guide rods, to which they are fastened by screws. In one rear view photograph two covers have been removed to show guide construction. No covers are provided for small panels as they are intended to carry no apparatus which would be affected by ordinary exposure. The dust covers are slotted at both ends to admit panel connecting cables to enter to the terminal blocks. All terminal blocks are designated in such manner that connections between panels can be made and checked with ease from circuit diagrams affixed to the inside of each cover.

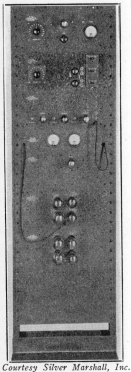

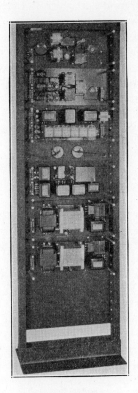

Courtesy Silver Marshall, Inc.

FIG. 152

S. M. RACK-AND-PANEL.

FIG. 152 A

"PA" AMPLIFIER.

Volume Indicator Panel. In the amplifier illustrated the top panel is type PA-60A VOLUME INDICATOR. It is completely AC operated and derives filament and plate current for its UY227 tube from the PA-40A POWER SUPPLY PANEL (fifth down from top). The VOLUME INDICATOR PANEL has, at the left, an input control graduated in 15 steps of 2 transmission units each for control of the voltage admitted for measurement. This voltage is measured across the output of the PA-20A INPUT AMPLIFIER (third from top) which is also the input to PA-30A OUTPUT AMPLIFIER PANELS (sixth and seventh from top). Signal volume level is indicated by the milliammeter at the right of the panel. The circuit is a special adaptation of the familiar vacuum tube voltmeter circuit, the calibration of the tube circuit being effected by means of the "BIAS" adjustment knob. A calibration for normal signal level is drawn into the meter scale with special level marks two transmission units above and below the normal value. These latter references give definite indication as to how much the level should be raised or lowered in operation to maintain a normal volume at a distant point. It should be noted here that the PA-60A VOLUME INDICATOR is of special service where the operator and amplifier are located in such position that he is unable to hear the actual reproduction of the system. Such a case is apt to occur in many installations; for example, where the equipment is located under the stage in an auditorium or at a racetrack. In such a case the operator would adjust the input to the PA-20A INPUT AMPLIFIER until an observer in the audience signalled that volume was correct. The operator would then turn up the VOLUME control on the PA-60A panel until the meter showed normal volume and on subsequent numbers of the program he would adjust the volume control on the INPUT CONTROL panel in such manner that the volume indicator meter showed that normal signal level was being maintained. The PA-60A panel is not always necessary, as a special monitoring circuit is provided in the output of PA-20A INPUT AMPLIFIER to which a loud-speaker may be connected for observation of signal level and quality by the operator.

Input Control Panel. A type PA-50A INPUT CON-TROL PANEL is next below the VOLUME INDI-CATOR. (This panel is but one of many that can be built to order to suit particular requirements.) This panel includes a control graduated in 15 units of 2 T.U.'s each to regulate the input to the amplifier from the various services, which in the PA-50A INPUT CONTROL PANEL are phonograph, radio, and the choice of either one of two microphone circuits. Three telephone keys, grouped on a Micarta subpanel at the right, control these services. The upper key has an OFF position in the center with RADIO and PHO-NOGRAPH at each of the side positions. The other two keys are for the respective microphone circuits and each has three positions, OFF, BAT., and TALK, these being the designations as engraved on the panel. In the OFF positions the battery circuits to the micro-phones are open, as well as the circuits to the volume control. When a key is moved to the BAT. position, the battery circuit to its microphone is completed but the microphone transformer is still disconnected from the INPUT AMPLIFIER to allow adjustment of microphone currents by means of the knobs adjacent to the key switches without interrupting another service in operation. In this way there is no interruption in the program while adjusting a microphone circuit. Microphone currents are measured by means of a plug from the PA-10A METER PANEL inserted in the jacks opposite the switching keys. A special circuit protects microphones from any inductive surges when opening or closing battery circuits.

PA-50A panel is but one of the types of input panels available. Special types can be had for a greater number, or different grouping, of services than are included in the PA-50A. Special mixing panels can be had for use with several microphones simultaneously, as when reproducing large orchestras. Similarly, special channels for operation out of telephone lines can be built to order when line characteristics are submitted with orders.

Input Amplifier Panel. Type PA-20A INPUT AMPLIFIER (Third down from top) is cross-connected to the PA-50A panel immediately above. This is a three-stage alternating current operated voltage amplifier, using one each UY227, UX226, and UX171A tubes in progression. The interestate coupling transformers are of the now well-known Clough tuned type manufactured by Silver-Marshall, Inc. They provide the best frequency characteristic known in the art and practically complete elimination of hysteretic distortion. The output circuit is of special design such that up to eight power stages of type PA-30A OUTPUT AMPLIFIER panels may be operated in parallel from it without diminution of volume or appreciable change in frequency characteristic.

The only adjustments necessary on the PA-20A

INPUT AMPLIFIER can be made from the panel and are the HUM-BALANCES so marked on the face. Great care has been exercised in the design of the AC features of this amplifier with the result that, in spite of its fine frequency characteristic (flat from 30 to above 4,000 cycles) as well as the total of four stages of audio amplification generally to be used in the system, hum from the alternating current supply can be balanced to a negligible value. The first two tubes of the amplifier are supported on special sponge rubber mountings so that noises from building vibrations, etc., will not be transmitted to the electrical system. This is important in the operation of Public Address Systems for surprisingly small spurious influences can greatly impair the signal intelligibility.

The condition of INPUT AMPLIFIER tubes can be checked by means of the PA-10A METER PANEL and plainly marked jacks in each tube circuit. (These, as well as all other jacks in the system are at panel potential with no exposed parts so that the danger of receiving an electrical shock through contact with any parts on panel face is eliminated.)

Test Meter Panel. Type PA-10A METER PANEL (fourth down from top) is a 4″ panel without dust cover carrying two milliammeters with flexible cords and plugs. These meters are used for checking microphone and tube currents, and keeping the entire system in proper operating condition. While the meter panel is not an absolute necessity for amplifier operation, at the same time its elimination is to be discouraged and it is recommended for all installations of S-M public address amplifying equipment.

Input Amplifier Power Supply Panel. Type PA-20A INPUT AMPLIFIER ordinarily operates from type PA-40A POWER SUPPLY PANEL (fifth down from top). This panel carries the necessary trans-

Courtesy Silver Marshall, Inc.

FIG. 153

S. M. PUBLIC ADDRESS UNIPAC.

formers for filament and plate supply operating in conjunction with a UX280 rectifier, as well as a large filter and the necessary isolation circuits for the operation of the high amplification system. No operating adjustments are necessary.

Output Amplifier Panel. In the typical amplifier illustrated, two PA-30A OUTPUT AMPLIFIERS are shown, although one will usually suffice for the largest auditoriums. (The two channels illustrated allow coverage of not one, but several auditoriums, as in a school or hotel.) Each PA-30A OUTPUT AMPLIFIER is completely self-contained with its own power supply consisting of a transformer for plate and filament voltages, two UX281 rectifier tubes, and the necessary filter condensers. Due to the push-pull amplifier circuit used, it is not only unnecessary but superfluous to employ chokes in the filter circuit. Their omission results in better regulation in the power supply, as well as a higher voltage applied to the amplifier tubes and does not affect hum, which is negligible in PA-30A OUTPUT AMPLIFIERS. An input transformer is included which permits the operation of up to eight PA-30A OUTPUT AMPLIFIERS from one PA-20A INPUT AMPLIFIER, as was noted above.

Each PA-30A OUTPUT AMPLIFIER employs two UX250 tubes operating at full rated plate voltage of 450 volts in a single stage power amplifier circuit. Under these conditions each tube in itself has an undistorted output of 4.65 watts, or 9.3 watts for the pair. Due to the push-pull circuit arrangement, normal grid excursions can be exceeded thus increasing the undistorted power output to a maximum of 15 watts (depending upon the nature of the output circuit). Increased output capacity can be effected by expansion to up to eight PA-30A panels for a large apartment, hospital, or school building, thus providing service for every room.

Type PA-30A OUTPUT AMPLIFIERS can be provided with output transformers to customer's order, either for operation into a group of magnetic speakers or a group of dynamic type reproducers, for indoor or outdoor service. In the latter case it is usual practice to provide transformers for operation directly into the moving coils of dynamic speaker units rather than into the transformers generally included in commercial speakers, thereby avoiding the transformation losses of additional transformers.

WESTERN ELECTRIC 555-W HORN

THE loud-speaking receiver used in connection with the projection of movietone is the Western Electric 555-W. This unit marks a distinct forward step in loud speaker construction, especially from the viewpoint of efficiency and volume of sound produced.

The diaphragm is made of thin aluminum alloy and the central portion is cupped into portions of two spherical surfaces, which gives it considerable stiffness and makes it move against the air column as a solid plunger. This diaphragm flexes only near its outer edge and gives considerably better results than the flat type of diaphragm that flexes throughout.

Driving is by means of a single layer coil of edge-wise wound aluminum ribbon, attached to the diaphragm and reacting with the field between the pole pieces of the field winding. The driving coil has high carrying capacity due to its single layer construction, small amount of insulating material, and consequent high rate of heat dissipation.

The cone shaped piece is located in front of the diaphragm to shape the tone chamber for proper distribution of the air pressure waves and this with the plunger-like motion of the diaphragm largely contributes to the high efficiency of the unit.

The efficiency in converting electrical energy into sound energy is very much higher than the ordinary horn unit or cone, 50% as against an average heretofore of only 1%. The power input that this unit will carry is likewise increased, 30 watts on continuous duty whereas the highest heretofore has been in the neighborhood of 5 watts. Combining these two factors it is seen that the sound output energy is 250 to 300 times that previously available, and certainly beyond all comparison with the usual home radio speaker units with which most of us are best acquainted.

In the use of these units it is important to make all connections exactly as called for, and of course all units will be connected the same way. If the connections are wrongly made so that the diaphragm of one unit is working in opposite direction to those of the others the sound waves will be in opposite phase, and quality will go galley-west.

When testing the units one at a time the horn control panel switch for the unit being tested should be set at 0, or full volume, with the fader turned low enough not to overload the unit. If a low volume setting at the distributor is used with a high fader setting, the volume may be the same but using only one horn the impedances of the circuits will not be balanced and quality will be poor. In testing the horn units it is well to compare the two lower units with each other, running one after the other or else both at once, and then do the same to compare the two upper units. In this way the balance between them will be verified and any incipient trouble will be detected much earlier than otherwise. In cases of failure the quality usually begins to suffer before complete failure occurs.

Under normal operation there should be very little trouble with these units, but under continued operation at excessive power something is bound to give way. Do not attempt to play an exit march at full volume through the house curtain which has just fallen. It can't be done except by raising not only the fader but also the amplifier gain control, and that is of course taboo.

Never operate the unit except in connection with a horn, as without the load of the long air column the diaphragm will be free to vibrate so violently as to break internal connections, loosen the coil, or cause damage to the diaphragm.

See that the nut that couples the unit to the horn is made up firmly, and be sure to keep the caps screwed on spare units and to store them in a dry place.

ELECTRO-DYNAMIC SPEAKERS

THE principle of the electro-dynamic drive was discovered by Ampere in 1820. Simply stated, it means that when a current-carrying conductor is placed in a magnetic field, there will be magnetic forces developed between the conductor and the magnet. A wire loop, suspended between the poles of the fixed magnet will move when current is sent through it, the direction and amplitude of motion depending upon the direction and strength of the current.

The electro-dynamic drive was used in horn type speakers for years before the inception of radio broadcasting. Its most highly developed form is probably in the driving unit for the large, horn type speakers made for Vitaphone and Movietone installations.

An electro-magnet is used because a sufficiently strong field cannot economically be supplied by permanent magnets. The field magnet has a round core and an iron head with a central circular opening which clears the core, leaving a ring-shaped air gap between these two members, across which there is a strong radial magnetic field. There is a cylindrical moving coil of perhaps 100 turns which is wound on a paper tube rigidly attached to the apex of the paper cone, and which is located in the ring-shaped air gap mentioned above. For high efficiency, the moving coil must as completely as possible fill the air gap without touching its sides, and this requirement calls for precision in manufacture. The moving coil and cone are maintained in position by flexible supports located near the coil and at the edge of the cone, the latter support usually consisting of an edging of thin leather. This method of suspension permits free to-and-fro motion of the cone, at the same time maintaining the moving coil clear of the sides of the air gap. It will be seen that if the field be excited by sending a direct current through its winding, and if current also be sent through the coil attached to the cone, the coil and cone will move. If this second current be an alternating, audio-frequency signal current, the movements of the coil will correspond in frequency and in amplitude to the variations in the signal current, the cone will be driven accordingly and will radiate sound.

The sole purpose of the baffle is to enable a relatively small cone to radiate low frequency sounds, and its presence is vitally necessary to the proper operation of such a speaker. For example, a six-inch cone without a baffle cannot radiate effectively below about 550 cycles, which is nearly an octave above middle C on the piano.

A rather crude and approximate explanation of baffle action follows. Suppose the cone to be executing, at a given instant, a forward movement. The air pressure immediately in front of the cone is increased, while the pressure immediately in the rear is decreased. The compressed air in front tends to slip around the edge of the cone into the rarefied region in the rear and, if it does this, the pressures become immediately equalized. No sound results, because sound consists of pressure differences propagated through the air as waves; that is, the pressure wave must be driven off by the cone, in order to produce sound.

Now suppose a baffle is added around the cone. The path from front to rear of the cone is now much longer than before and, assuming the cone to move forward, the air cannot avoid the forward thrust of the cone by slipping around the edge because it encounters the baffle, and is therefore impelled forward as a sound wave. A popular way of stating this action is that the baffle allows the cone to get a grip on the air.

At high frequencies, where the waves are short compared with the cone diameter, a baffle is unnecessary, but at low frequencies, with their consequent long sound waves, the path from front to rear of the cone must be made correspondingly long.

The baffle may take the form of a widely flaring cone or pyramid. It will be seen that a larger effective baffle with a given size of face may be obtained with the box baffle, as compared with the flat type. The box baffle, however, has the disadvantage that the enclosure of the sides forms a cavity behind the cone which tends to resonate at low frequencies and to give the speaker a barrel tone. This effect is particularly bad if the box is deep or it is partially closed at the rear. Such speakers must not be set close to a wall unless the sides are freely vented and even then, bad resonances may occur.

Electro-dynamic speakers, even when mounted in flat baffles, have comparatively strong resonances at certain low frequencies. The baffle should be heavy enough so as not to vibrate readily. Some of the cabinet type electro-dynamic speakers we have tested had cabinets with thin plywood sides which vibrated strongly and gave these speakers an unpleasant barrel tone.

In order that an electro-dynamic loud-speaker may operate properly, it must be provided with certain other accessories. For instance, from three to twenty-five watts direct current are required for field excitation. The stronger the field, the more sensitive the speaker.

In order to obtain high sensitivity with a low exciting current, the clearance between the moving coil and the pole pieces must be cut down, resulting in increased manufacturing difficulty and liability to operating trouble, therefore the tendency of present manufacturers seems to be toward the use of safer clearances and larger field currents.

Field power may be derived from a storage battery, from a rectifier, which may be part of a power supply unit for a receiving set or amplifier, or it may be supplied from an individual rectifier designed for the purpose. In this day of light-socket operated receivers, the storage battery is out of the question. If power is to be supplied from the second source mentioned above, the field magnet is usually wired into the circuit in place of one of the "B" choke coils. As the field may require as much as 150 milliamperes at 100 volts in such cases, it is necessary that the rectifier be specially designed to supply this power, as well as that required by the receiving set or amplifier. This method allows for a very low excitation of the field—about four watts. Greater input from the receiver, therefore, is required for a given volume in the loud-speaker.

The third method, that of employing an individual rectifier for the loud-speaker field, affords a high excitation of the field—about seventeen watts. This makes the sensitivity greater than that of any of the so-called magnetic speakers, thus giving a wealth of volume with a small size power tube, the UX-171. Practically all other designs of dynamic speakers use a smaller rectifier, giving approximately six watts for field excitation. This requires larger power tubes in the receiver to give the same loud-speaker volume.

The principal advantages of the electro-dynamic

speaker, as compared with the moving iron type, are as follows:

1. By proper construction and the use of a large baffle, very low frequencies can be reproduced.

2. The impedance does not change greatly with frequency. This simplifies the problem of getting sufficient power into the speaker over the whole frequency range.

3. It has, when carefully made, a high load capacity without serious distortion.

S-M DYNAMIC SPEAKER UNITS
AC AND DC

In the illustration herewith is pictured the 850 type speaker, which consists essentially of a high-permeability iron pot containing a core and a field magnetizing coil, and carrying a steel spider frame housing the cone diaphragm to which is attached a "voice" coil suspended in the field of the pot magnet. This assembly is termed the "head" and is the complete loud-speaker unit in itself. It requires, however, certain accessories before it may be used with an ordinary radio set, and in the model illustrated, the head is attached by mounting brackets to a steel base which carries a universal output transformer and a power supply unit to provide direct current for the field magnet coil. In the 850 type speaker this power supply unit operates directly from a 105 to 120 volt, 50 to 60 cycle AC lamp socket, while in the 851 speaker the power supply and its base are omitted entirely, the 1900 ohm field magnet coil in this case being intended to be connected to a source of 90 to 120 volt direct current such as is obtained from a radio set B eliminator, or from inclusion of the field coil as a choke in the filter circuit of a B power supply.

The above description of the 850 AC and 851 DC speakers is applicable to almost any good dynamic speaker. There are certain features, however, found in the S-M dynamic speakers but found in no other speakers today.

Most important among these improvements are the several that tend to make the S-M dynamic the finest low frequency reproducer available today. Theoreti-

cally, all dynamics are excellent low note reproducers—
actually, practically few standard AC types are as good
as the average magnetic cone. This is because, to obtain AC operation, general practice has been to supply
field current at 6 to 10 volts and about ½ ampere by
means of a 110 volt step-down transformer and a con-
tact-type of dry-plate rectifier, and without any filtration. Even with new rectifier units, the AC ripple in
the DC output is so great that a bad 60 and 120 cycle
hum is heard in the speaker as soon as power from the
rectifier is fed to the field coil. Filtration of low voltage, high current DC is not an easy problem—it is expensive, and, with the erratic performance observed in
many dry-contact rectifiers, often impossible in practice. But since the market demanded AC operation, so
there came into general use the scheme of employing
a small "bucking" or "neutralizing" coil located close to
the moving voice coil and so connected as to "buck" out
or "neutralize" 60 and 120 cycle AC hum. In practice
this popular arrangement not only cuts out (or down)
AC hum, but it does likewise to signals of hum frequency, with the net result that the average AC dynamic speaker is far from ideal at those low frequencies.
Further than this, the fairly erratic operation of the
dry-contact rectifiers, and their proneness to develop
high "back-currents," has resulted in the condition
where most AC dynamics often hum more than an AC
receiver with which they may be used. Fig. 155 is a
photograph of the S-M dynamic speaker.

This condition has been entirely avoided in the S-M
850 AC dynamic through the use of a high voltage, low
current field winding, power to which is supplied by a
rectifier employing the dependable and stable UX280
(CX380) rectifier tube. This tube operates in connec-

tion with a full wave transformer having a 5 volt filament winding and two 150 volt secondaries, to deliver
120 volts DC to the speaker field, which is rendered so
pure by a 2 mfd. filter condenser and the choking action

Courtesy of Silver Marshall, Inc.

FIG. 155

S. M. DYNAMIC SPEAKER.

of the high inductance field coil itself as to eliminate
the usual annoying AC hum in the speaker itself. This
arrangement obviously does not require a "bucking" or

"neutralizing" coil, and hence the low note response of the speaker at 60 and 120 cycles is superior to that of any other standard AC dynamic units.

Through careful design the need for the usual corrective tone filters found in most dynamics to iron out resonances (and, incidentally, much of the high response as well) has been avoided—no such correctives are found in S-M dynamics. In consequence, the frequency response of the 850 and 851 speakers, in direct comparative tests, has been found superior to practically all competitive units, the S-M dynamic units operating substantially uniformly from 30 to 5,000 cycles or more.

Each S-M unit is equipped with a universal output transformer of wide application. This transformer is designed to operate from a push-pull amplifier using two UX171A (CX371A), two UX250 (CX350) or two of the new intermediate power tubes at maximum efficiency, and is of the same general characteristics as the transformer employed in the expensive one and two thousand dollar S-M rack-and-panel amplifiers. From this transformer is taken out a special tap at the exact point to provide most efficient operation out of one 171A, 250, or out of the new intermediate power tube while the whole primary winding matches a 210 tube for conditions of maximum undistorted output. The transformer is designed to avoid core saturation at the plate currents of one or two UX250 tubes, and this accounts in a measure for the unusual purity of reproduction of the S-M dynamic units.

While these units are ideal for home operation, the very characteristics that make them so have been accentuated to make them particularly suited to public address work at high powers. Each unit is recommended to dissipate two to three watts of signal energy for theatre, auditorium, or outdoor use. For such work, combinations of one or two baffles, four to six feet square and ten inches deep, made of ⅞" lumber, are recommended, with from one to four dynamic units closely grouped in the centre of the baffle. For 500 to 1,000 seat theatres, one or two units in individual baffles are recommended when fed by one UX250 in an amplifier. For 1,000 to 2,000 seat theatres, fed by two 250 tubes in push-pull, two baffles, each with two to four units, are recommended. For larger theatres, of 2,000 to 4,000 seats, two to three baffles each, carrying two to four speaker units, and fed from one or two 250 push-pull output amplifier stages (such as S-M PA-30A amplifier panels) will give tone quality and volume equal to that of most "talkie" installations.

The S-M 850 AC dynamic unit is for operation from any 105 to 120 volt, 50 to 60 cycle AC lamp socket and is equipped with universal output transformer for single or push-pull output amplifier stages. It requires one UX280 (CX380) tube for operation, is 9" outside diameter (to fit 8¾" baffle hole) 6⅝" deep, 10" wide over power unit, and weighs about 15 pounds.

Type 851 speaker is identical, except that it is intended to obtain field current of 40 to 50 m. a. from a 90 to 120 volt DC source, such as a B eliminator, or through inclusion as a choke in a power supply (as in S-M 678PD amplifier). It is not equipped with power supply or base.

FIG. 156

A BANK OF RCA LOUD-SPEAKERS MOUNTED ON A MOVABLE
TRUCK (NOTE DIFFERENT ANGLES OF SPEAKERS).

RCA LOUDSPEAKER

RCA PHOTOPHONE loud-speakers are of the electro-dynamic cone type and were selected after extensive tests of all present day loud-speaking equipment. Each cone is 12 inches in diameter and is mounted with a special suspension so that there is absolute freedom of motion of the cone. The number of loud-speakers in use in any installation will depend upon the type of amplifying equipment installed and is of course governed by the size of the house and its acoustic qualities. Reproducing equipment is supplied in several types, one type to operate each combination of 4, 8, 12 and 16 loud-speakers. The loud-speakers are mounted in groups on the side and above the screen and directed into the auditorium in such a way as to secure practically perfect sound distribution.

Four methods of mounting the loud-speakers are available. In theatres devoted to motion pictures only, the loud-speakers will be mounted permanently. In theatres where it is necessary that the loud-speakers be removed from the stage, three types of mountings are available. In one of these the loud-speakers are mounted on each side of the screen on racks, portable on rollers, so that they may be removed to a point behind the wings when not in use. The second method of mounting is that in which the loud-speakers are of the fly type so that they may be pulled up above the stage at the same time that the screen is raised. For the third type RCA Photophone manufactures a special frame for a combination screen and speaker mounting. The screen and loud-speakers are then installed so that they may be flied as a single unit. In some installations those speakers which are located alongside the screen may be mounted portable on rollers and those above the screen may be mounted either permanently or flied. The method of installing the loud-speakers will depend upon the type of theatre and the desires of the management.

The loud-speakers are mounted in a heavy wood baffle board which aids in the reproduction of all frequencies and in securing perfect sound distribution throughout the theatre. There are two types of loud-speaker units, one being that in which the plane of the loud-speaker cone makes an angle of 45 degrees with the baffle board, and the other being that in which the plane of the cone makes an angle of 15 degrees with the baffle board. These loud-speaker units may be mounted so that the individual speakers are pointing in a number of directions, thus preventing any directional effect. In theatres which have exceptionally high ceilings or two balconies, two or more of the loud-speakers may be turned upward so that the volume of sound in the balconies will be the same as that on the main floor.

It is difficult to produce by one or two speakers of the horn type a uniform distribution of sound since the horn type speakers produce a narrow beam of sound and result in areas of varying intensities in the theatre. The cone type speaker radiates sound over a very great angle, then by employing a great number of these speakers properly located about the picture screen, uniform volume is produced about the entire theatre and all directional effects are cancelled. The result is that the sound appears to come from the screen itself. In addition, the cone type speaker responds to all frequencies, thus giving more faithful reproduction of sound. The horn type speaker has a natural period of vibration within its air column and the speaker responds more readily to frequencies within this range. The result is that there will be some frequencies which will reproduce with greater intensity than others and producing very undesirable distortion of sounds.

In each type of installation made by RCA Photophone the loud-speakers are controlled entirely from the projection room. Provision is made so that if any trouble develops in a loud-speaker or a bank of loud-speakers this particular group of speakers can be removed from service and the show continued with the remaining groups.

Courtesy RCA Photophone

FIG. 157

TWO MOVING COIL RCA LOUD-SPEAKERS.

FIG. 158

LOUD-SPEAKER BANKS LOCATED AT EACH SIDE OF SCREEN AND
SO ARRANGED THAT THE SPEAKERS FLY WITH MOTION PICTURE
SCREEN.

SCREENS FOR SOUND WORK

ONE of the most serious problems at present encountered in the projection of talking pictures is the elimination of the excessive loss of light which results from the use of a porous screen.

The mere fact that the screen is porous, regardless of the degree of porosity, is a sufficient indication that some loss of light is entailed. The extent of this light loss will naturally be in proportion to the degree of porosity.

At the present time, special screens, consisting of a single piece of loosely woven fabric, are being used in most of the talking picture installations. The attempt is made to achieve an apparently solid surface, which still is porous to sound waves, by so weaving the cloth that loose ends of threads will form a fine fuzz on the projection surface so as to cover, to a great extent the spaces between the main threads which constitute the foundation of the cloth.

The effect obtained is that of a coarsely woven rug, having a fairly long nap which gives it the appearance of being solidly woven when in reality, the opposite is true. As a first endeavor to meet two opposite requirements, this screen represents a fairly creditable job in that it possesses the essential qualities of fair picture registration and good sound transmission.

As an ultimate objective in the way of a talking picture screen, however, it falls too far short in the matter of projection efficiency to give it serious consideration.

In the first place, the initial reflection efficiency of

this screen is too low to meet present conditions of projection in theatres. It has been officially claimed for this screen that its initial reflection factor is about 80 per cent. This is manifestly impossible because the reflection factor for a new opaque screen, either of the flat white or metallic type, is seldom above 80 per cent.

Upon investigating this claim of 80 per cent for the porous cloth screen we are informed that this applies to the reflection factor of the cloth only and does not take into consideration the inactive area represented by the blank spaces between the threads so that the reflection factor claimed for this screen as a whole, must be lower.

Without having definite figures to support our contention, we should place the overall efficiency of this screen somewhere between 60 and 70 per cent as this would seem to be more reasonable for a screen of this nature.

Upon this basis alone, this particular type of porous screen presents a serious drawback to satisfactory projection because many theatres have no reserve illumination to draw upon in order to restore the overall brilliancy of the picture to its former value.

If a proper reserve of illumination were available, the inefficiency of the porous screen would not be so serious, at least from a light standpoint. Other factors present themselves, however, to further complicate the matter.

Aside from the low initial reflection efficiency of the porous cloth screen, the most serious objection to its use rests on the fact that it depreciates with almost inconceivable rapidity as compared with the hitherto commonly used opaque screens.

The reason for this is found in the dust collecting

properties of the "fuzz" which constitutes the projection surface. The many fine thread ends which serve to cover the interstices between the foundation threads form a most excellent dust trap and no better location for such a screen, from a dust collecting standpoint, could be found than its location on the stage. Air currents, caused by moving draw curtains, raising and lowering of the screen and drop curtains, organ pipes, heated stage lighting equipment and numerous other props, serve to keep the concentrated dust at the front of the house in constant motion so that eventually most of it finds a comfortable lodging place on the fibres of the porous screen. Once this dust is imbedded in the fibres it cannot be removed by ordinary cleaning processes.

Various projectionists and observers have claimed that the porous cloth screen depreciates from a white to a slate gray color in a period of time estimated at from 3 to 6 months depending upon dust conditions in the particular theatre. The depreciation is said to be so bad as to justify replacing the screen with a new one after a period, not exceeding 6 months. If this is true, and it seems reasonable that it would be, then the low initial reflection efficiency of the screen coupled with its rapid deterioration would condemn it as a permanent fixture on the stage.

A low reflection efficiency is not the only objection to this screen. It has little to offer in the way of registration qualities. For excellent registration each little pinpoint over the entire active area of the screen must reflect a cone of light to the seating area. Each one of these thousands of little cones must cover the entire seating area.

If even small portions of the active screen area are

missing, corresponding areas of the picture image will also be missing so that poor registration of the image will result. The effect of perforations in the screen is the same as that observed (but to a lesser degree) when one looks at an object through a wire screen. The cross wires composing the screen hide portions of the object from direct view and result in indistinct vision.

It is a fact, determined from observation in theatres that the porous cloth screen presents an image which is not as sharply defined and distinct as that observed on a section of an opaque screen placed beside it.

The need for a porous screen arises from the location of the horns directly behind the screen. The reason given for so placing the horns is that a better illusion of directional tonal effects is thereby obtained.

There is much contention with respect to this claim so that it cannot be definitely said that it is true or not true.

Any other placement of the horns (than directly behind the screen) would eliminate the need for a porous screen and so would restore the projected picture to its former high state of brightness and definition. This consideration alone, is sufficient to warrant serious thought toward finding another location for the horns. If the difference in illusion is slight between speaker locations as behind the screen and elsewhere, then it would be better to forego the slight benefit of this directional effect in order to gain the tremendous benefits of good picture registration and increased picture brightness.

FILM SPLICERS

THE importance of correct splicing of sound movie film cannot be overestimated. Poor splicing means poor reproduction. It will be as well for the projectionist to equip himself with a good film splicer. There are a number of these on the market, including the one made by the Bell & Howell Company of Chicago and that made by the Griswold Company.

The Griswold splicer has a stationary double shear blade located over the centre of the base, on each side of which is a swinging film clamp comprising upper and lower jaws, on the lower jaw of each clamp is attached a shear blade to coact with a stationary double shear blade so that a section of film placed in the right film clamp may be sheared by the shear blade carried by the left clamp, and a section placed in the left film clamp may be sheared by the shear blade carried by the right film clamp, thus the two sections of film after shearing will overlap the width of the lower shear blade.

An automatic clamping device is employed to hold upper and lower jaws firmly down on stop. This device provides for raising the upper jaw without disturbing the lower jaw. When the jaws carrying the film are raised this device clamps the film firmly between the jaws.

To the upper right jaw is attached a means for pressing together the overlapping portions of film and on the left upper jaw is a guard and gauge.

When applying cement to the film carried in the left jaws, the jaws should be raised to bring the film away from the double shear blade which prevents the cement being carried by capillary attraction to the under side of film.

Another feature which is of great advantage is the facility in placing correctly the sections of film in the film clamps.

Directly below the double stationary shear blade is a flash light controlled by a switch located on the front of the base, this lighting device is of great assistance in matching difficult sections of film, especially when machine is used in poorly lighted room.

The battery, lamp and bottle of film cement are easily accessible by removing a plate held to the base by a thumbscrew, the bottle of film cement is held firmly in the front right corner of the base as will be seen in illustration with only the neck of the bottle protruding above the base. The method of holding the bottle is very satisfactory because of the convenient location, ease in removing cork and brush and protection from breakage.

Each machine is provided with an emulsion scraper, having a blade which can be changed in eight positions for the purpose of obtaining the greatest usefulness from the blade.

The base is black japan, and fittings are bright nickel, which combination contrasts and makes a very pleasing appearance.

FILM SPEED INDICATOR

AMONG the projection room necessities ushered in through the adoption of sound pictures, none is more vitally essential than a film speed indicator. The effective synchronization of music or speech through the picture demands absolute film control on the part of the operator. It is obviously essential that such control can be attained only through the use of a dependable and accurate indicator for film speed.

It is significant that a projectionist, fully appreciating the need for such a device and the technical difficulties that must be overcome in its making, should design and perfect a film speed indicator at a price that pre-destines it to universal installation.

The new Strong Film Speed Indicator is accurately calibrated to show both number of film feet per minute and the minutes consumed per thousand feet of film. The dial is lettered in clear numerals and is easily read at a glance from any angle—an important feature, definitely superior to most such devices formerly available.

The working mechanism of the indicator head is manufactured exclusively for the Essannay Electric Manufacturing Co. by one of the largest makers of speedometers and similar merchandise in the world. It can be readily adapted to installation on any model projector. The purchaser indicates the type of machine he is using and the Strong Film Speed Indicator comes to him ready for immediate installation on his particular model of projector.

It is as nearly fool-proof as any mechanical device can be and is constructed for years of reliable use. Its accuracy is guaranteed.

Another device manufactured by the Essannay Electric Company and a necessity in the projection rooms of theatres showing talking movies, is the Electric **Change-Over.**

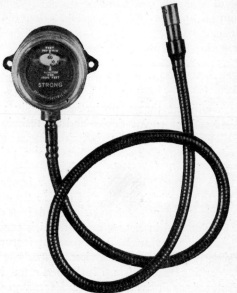

Courtesy Essannay Mfg. Co.

FIG. 159

FILM SPEED INDICATOR.

These devices allow the discarding of the old unsightly strings, wires, rods, etc., and the old slip-shod hand change, and substitute a method whereby a change is made that cannot be seen on the screen, and is absolutely noiseless, allowing the picture to continue with no interruption.

The devices consist of a panel 6x10 inches, with a 3-inch hole through which your picture is projected.

This hole is covered with two metal blades, working on the same plan as a pair of scissors, the opening and closing of which is electrically controlled, the pushing of a button opening one and closing the other simultaneously.

These devices all mounted over port opening in front

MOUNTING FOR STRONG CHANGEOVER ON BRENKERT F4 EFFECT MACHINE

Courtesy Essannay Mfg. Co.

FIG. 160

of each machine and to make a change it is merely necessary to start your machine and push a button, which opens one device and closes the other. Devices are connected together by necessary wiring, and allow you to have a change-over device that is absolutely unfailing, and allows the discarding of all strings, rods, etc.

With these devices you can equip a battery of three machines and a double dissolve stero and go from any machine to any other, or from any machine to either stero and back again, as for instance, you are running feature and going back and forth from machine No. 1 to No. 2, then to No. 3, then back to No. 1, then to No. 2. Finishing feature on No. 2 you press button and cut off No. 2 and let on slide, going back and forth from upper to lower stero, and finishing slides, you have weekly in No. 3 machine. Going to No. 3 you start machine and press button and reel is on and slide off.

You can have any combination you want and it is not necessary to make any previous set-up, as there is a button at each machine or stero, and the pressing of that button opens that device only and closes any that may be open. Extension switches can be mounted at any desired point in the booth.

STORAGE BATTERIES

IN the proper care of a storage battery if the following things are remembered you will escape 75 per cent of your battery troubles:

First—Test the specific gravity of all cells with a hydrometer two or three times a month. If any of the cells are below 1,200, the battery is more than half discharged, and it should be recharged.

Second—Pure water must be added to all cells regularly and at sufficiently frequent intervals to keep the solution at the proper height. Add water until solution is one-half inch above top of plates.

Never let solution get below top of plates.

Plugs must be removed to add water, then replaced and screwed on after filling.

The battery should be inspected and filled with water once every week in warm weather and once every two weeks in cold weather.

Do not use Acid or Electrolyte, only pure water.

Do not use any water known to contain even small quantities of salts or iron of any kind.

Distilled water or fresh, clean rain water only should be used.

Use only a clean vessel for handling or storing water.

Add water regularly, although the battery may seem to work all right without it.

In order to avoid freezing of the battery, it should always be kept in a fully charged condition. A fully charged battery will not freeze in temperatures ordinarily met.

Electrolyte will freeze as follows:

Sp. gr. 1,150, battery empty, 20 above zero F.
Sp. gr. 1,180, battery ¾ discharged, zero F.
Sp. gr. 1,215, battery ½ discharged, 20 below zero F.
Sp. gr. 1,250 battery ¼ discharged, 60 below zero F.

Therefore, it will be seen that there is no danger of the battery freezing up if it is kept at a specific gravity of from 1,250 to 1,300 and it should be kept as near 1,275 as possible. Under no circumstances should acid or electrolyte be added to the cells to bring them up to the required specific gravity. Nothing but pure water must be put in the cells after the battery has been once placed in commission and the specific gravity must be kept up by charging only.

General Storage Battery Data. A storage battery, secondary battery, or accumulator, as it is variously called, is an electrical device in which chemical action is first caused by the passage of electric current, after which the device is capable of giving off electric current by means of secondary reversed chemical action. Any voltaic couple that is reversible in its action is a storage battery. The process of storing electric energy by the passage of current from an external source, is called charging the battery; when the battery is giving off current, it is said to be discharging. A storage battery cell has two elements or plates, and an electrolyte. The two plates are usually made of the same material, though they may be of two different materials.

Polarity. The terms positive and negative are employed to designate the direction of the flow of current to or from the battery; that is, the positive plate is the one from which the current flows on discharge, and the negative plate is the one into which current flows on discharge. In a lead battery the positive plate, on which the lead peroxide is formed, has a comparatively hard surface of a reddish-brown or chocolate color, while the negative plate, which carries the sponge lead, has a much softer surface of a grayish color.

Electrolyte. The electrolyte used with the lead type of battery is aways a diluted solution of sulphuric acid. The specific gravity of the electrolyte when the battery is fully charged, varies from about 1.210 for stationary batteries to 1.300 for automobile ignition batteries and other portable batteries.

The proper specific gravity to use varies with the conditions, and the specific gravity may be found by the use of a hydrometer. When the cells of the battery are fully charged, the specific gravity of the electrolyte, as indicated by the hydrometer, should be 1275 to 1300 at 70 degrees F. The final density is the usual practice. None but sulphur or brimstone acid should be used. When diluting, the acid should be poured into the water slowly and with great caution.

Never Pour the Water Into the Acid. The specific gravity of commercial sulphuric acid is 1.835, and 1 part of such acid should be mixed with 5 parts (by volume) of pure water. Care should be taken that no impurities enter the mixture. The vessel used for the mixing must be a lead-lined tank or one of wood that has never contained any other acid; a wooden wash-tub or spirits barrel answers very well. The electrolyte when placed in the cell should come ½ inch above the top of the plates. Before putting the electrolyte in the cells, the positive pole of each cell should be connected to the negative pole of the next cell in the series and the whole battery of cells should be connected, through a main switch, to the charging source—the positive pole of the battery to the positive side of the charging source, and the negative pole of the negative side. After adding the electrolyte the battery should be charged at once or at least inside of 2 hours. A little pure water should be added occasionally to the electrolyte to make up for evaporation, and a small quantity of acid should be added about once a year to make up for that thrown off in the form of spray or that absorbed by the sediment in the cells. Do not use anything but pure distilled water in storage batteries because any impurities such as those commonly found in tap or well water will in a very short time absolutely ruin the battery.

Test of Specific Gravity. The specific gravity of the electrolyte is the most accurate guide as to the state of charge of a leadtype storage battery. The test of the specific gravity is made by means of a hydrometer having a suitable scale for the type of cell to be tested. In all portable types of batteries, and ordinarily in vehicle batteries it is usually necessary to draw some of the electrolyte from the cell in order to test its specific gravity with the hydrometer, which should have a scale reading from 1150 to 1300.

Charging. The normal charging rate is the same as the 8-hour discharge rate specified by manufacturers. The charge should be continued uninterruptedly until complete; but if repeatedly carried beyond the full-charge point, unnecessary waste of energy, a waste of acid through spraying, a rapid accumulation of sediment, and a shortened life of the plates will result. At the end of the first charge, it is advisable to discharge the battery about one-half, and then immediately recharge it. It is advisable to overcharge the batteries slightly about once a week, in order that the prolonged gassing may thoroughly stir up the electrolyte and also to correct inequalities in the voltages of the cells. If the discharge rate is very low, or if the battery is seldom used, it should be given a freshening charge weekly.

Indications of a Complete Charge. A complete charge should be from 12 to 15 per cent greater in ampere-hours than the preceding discharge. The principal indications of a complete charge are: (1) The voltage reaches a maximum value of 2.4 to 2.7 per cell, and the specific gravity of the electrolyte a maximum of 1275 to 1300 per cell. If all the cells are in good condition and the charging current is constant, maximum voltage and specific gravity are reached when there is no further increase for $\frac{1}{4}$ to $\frac{1}{2}$ hour; (2) the amount of gas given off at the plates increases and the electrolyte assumes a milky appearance, or is said to boil.

Voltage Required. The voltage at the end of a charge depends on the age of the plates, the temperature of the electrolyte, and the rate of charging; at normal rate of charge and at normal temperature, the voltage at the end of the charge of a newly installed battery will be 2.5 volts per cell or higher; as the age of the battery increases, the point at which it will be fully charged is gradually lowered and may drop as low as 2.4 volts. All voltage readings are taken with the current flowing; readings taken with the battery on open circuit are of little value and are frequently misleading. After the completion of a charge and when the current is off, the voltage per cell will drop rapidly to 2.05 volts and remain there for some time while the battery is on open circuit. When the discharge is started, there will be a further drop to 2 volts, or slightly less, after which the decrease will be slow. Cells should never be charged at the maximum rate except in cases of emergency.

Direction of Current. The charging current must always flow through the battery from the positive pole to the negative pole. If it is necessary to test the polarity of the line wires when no instruments are available, attach two wires to the mains, connect some resistance in series to limit the current, and dip the free ends of the wires into a glass of acidulated water, keeping the ends about 1 inch apart. Bubbles are given off most freely from the negative end.

Discharging. Heavy overcharging rates maintained for a considerable time, are almost sure to injure the cells. The normal discharge rate should not be exceeded except in case of emergency. The amount of charge remaining available at any time can be determined from voltage and specific-gravity readings. During the greater part of a complete discharge, the drop in voltage is slight and very gradual; but near the end the falling off becomes much more marked. Under no circumstances should a battery ever be discharged below 1.7 volts per cell, and in ordinary service it is advisable to stop the discharge at 1.75 or 1.8 volts. If a reserve is to be kept in the battery for use in case of emergency, the discharge must be stopped at a correspondingly higher voltage. The fall in density of the electrolyte is in direct proportion to the ampere-hours

Courtesy United Artists Studio

FIG. 162

BATTERY ROOM AT UNITED ARTISTS STUDIO. THERE ARE
ELEVEN MASTER BATTERIES WHICH ARE USED FOR TWO SOUND
STAGES.

taken out, and is therefore a reliable guide as to the amount of discharge.

Restoring Weakened Cells. There are several methods of restoring cells that have become low: (1) Overcharge the whole battery until the low cells are brought up to the proper point, being careful not to damage other cells in the battery; (2) cut the low cells out of circuit during one or two discharges and in again during charge; (3) give the defective cells an individual charge. Before putting a cell that has been defective into service again, care should be taken to see that all the signs of a full charge are present.

Sediment in Cells. During service, small particles drop from the plates and accumulate on the bottom of the cells. This sediment should be carefully watched, especially under the middle plates, where it accumulates most rapidly, and should never be allowed to touch the bottom of the plates and thus short-circuit them. If there is any free space at the end of the cells, the sediment can be raked from under the plates and then scooped up with a wooden ladle or other nonmetallic device. If this method is impracticable, the electrolyte, after the battery has been fully charged, should be drawn off into clean containing vessels; the cells should then be thoroughly washed with water until all the sediment is removed, and the electrolyte should be replaced at once before the plates have had a chance to become dry. In addition to the electrolyte withdrawn, new electrolyte must be added to fill the space left by the removal of the sediment; the new electrolyte should be of 1.3 or 1.4 sp. gr. in order to counteract the effect of the water absorbed by the plates while being washed. If at any time any impurities, especially any metal other than lead or any acid other than sulphuric acid, gets into a cell, the electrolyte should be emptied at once and the cells thoroughly washed and filled with pure electrolyte.

Idle Batteries. If a battery is to be idle for, say 6 months or more, it is usually best to withdraw the electrolyte, as follows: After giving a complete charge, siphon or pump the electrolyte into convenient receptacles, preferably carboys that have previously been cleaned and have never been used for any other kind of acid. As each cell is emptied, immediately refill it with water; when all the cells are filled, begin discharging and continue until the voltage falls to or below 1 volt per cell at normal load, and then draw off the water.

Putting Battery into Commission. To put an idle battery in commission, first make sure that the connections are right for charging; then remove the water, put in the electrolyte, and begin charging at once at the normal rate. From 25 to 30 hours continuous charging will be required to give a complete charge.

Sulphating. Lead sulphate is practically an insulator. Some of this material is formed in all lead-sulphuric-acid storage cells on discharge and is reconverted to lead oxide or lead peroxide on recharging the cell. If present in excessive quantities, the sulphate adheres to the plates, especially the positive, in white soluble patches, preventing chemical action, increasing the resistance of the cell, and causing unequal mechanical stresses that may buckle the plates. The most frequent causes of sulphating are overdischarging, too high specific gravity of electrolyte, and allowing the battery to stand for a considerable length of time in a discharged condition.

THE TELEGRAPHONE

THE telegraphone, as an instrument for recording and reproducing music and speech, is known to most electrical engineers who have interested themselves in sound, but it remains relatively unknown to the layman.

The telegraphone makes use of an electro-magnetic principle of recording and reproducing. In its best known form a wire of steel, several miles in length, is passed by, and in contact with, the poles of electro-magnets, at considerable speed. The coils of the magnets are in circuit with a telephone transmitter or microphone. As the fluctuating currents in this circuit pass thru the coils they induce magnetism in the soft iron cores which constitute the poles, the magnetism varying with the current. As the wire passes the poles, magnetic charges are induced in the wire, and these charges constitute the record of the sound. When the wire is run back and then passed forward past the pole pieces again, a different circuit is employed and the currents which are induced in the coils, as the magnetic charges of the passing wire change the magnetism of the poles of the magnet, are carried to a telephone receiver where they actuate a diaphragm in exactly the same way as in a telephone.

It will readily appear that the magnets, their poles and the wire constitute the heart of the machine. The rest is but a mechanical contrivance to wind the wire from one spool to another. The magnets are housed in what is called a "talking head," and this instrument is the critical part of the machine. The pole pieces must be of soft iron, the wire must be of steel. The pole pieces must be of a certain thickness, and, since they operate in pairs (the members of a pair being on opposite sides of the wire) they must be "staggered" to produce the best results. The "staggering" seems to work best at .035 inch. The wire used is hard piano wire .01 inch in thickness. This wire can, of course, be of any desired length, standard equipment being sufficient to operate the machine continuously for about thirty minutes.

In the machines supplied by the factory the spools for the wire are driven by an electric motor. The "talking head" is located between the spools and is moved up and down by means of a heart-cam, thus guiding the winding and unwinding of the wire so that it will not "pile up" on the spools. The wire, as it passes through the "talking head," makes contact with two pairs of magnet poles. The first pair acts as an erasing agent, clearing the wire of all previous records. The second pair plants the desired record on the wire by transverse magnetization. Electric controls make it possible to start, stop and reverse the motion of the spools by simply pushing the proper buttons on the control set. This set, of course, can be placed at any desired distance from the recording machine. The control set has a dial for indicating the position of the wire, so that when a record has been made the wire can be run back to the place from which it started.

A plug in the control set makes it possible to connect an ordinary telephone with the apparatus, so that a telephone conversation can be recorded. By means of the same plug it is possible to record from a radio receiving set, or from a phonograph record by means of a "pick-up."

It is a simple matter to substitute a radio microphone

for the telephone transmitter, and to substitute an amplifier and loud-speaker for the ordinary head phones by which the record is usually heard.

Since the machine was designed for stenographic dictation, suitable foot controls were evolved for the use of the typist.

In order to preserve a section of record after it is made, a device was developed that automatically stops the backward motion of the spools at any desired point, thus making it impossible to erase that part of the record back of this point so long as this device remains set. If it is desirable to preserve a whole wire-length record, the spools can readily be removed by means of a "lifter" and another set substituted. The record seems to be fairly permanent so long as the record wire is kept in a dry place so that it will not rust.

The theoretical advantage of this method of recording over other known methods is that it gets away from the distorting effects of mechanical parts. A needle which writes in wax possesses, in common with all material bodies, inertia, momentum, and friction. Thus it takes some of the energy which should go into the record to start the needle, it takes some more to stop and reverse its direction, and still more to overcome the resistance of the wax in which it cuts its groove. Light recording gets away from the friction of the writing pencil, but labors under the distorting effects of momentum and inertia. The electro-magnetic principle escapes from all three of these limitations. Between the disc of the microphone and the disc of the loud-speaker there is no mechanical principle, and hence no material inertia, momentum or friction to overcome. Theoretically, all of the energy goes into the record and there should be less distortion than in any other type of recording device. The fact that electro-magnetic recording is not as perfect as it might be may fairly be laid, it would seem, to lack of skilled engineering or else to lack of serious desire to perfect this type of recording. Possibly there are insurmountable difficulties involved in the circuits and magnets, but the writer has had no evidence presented to him that serious effort has been made to determine what they are or how to overcome them. It is believed by many of us that, with sufficient research and experiment, this method could be made more perfect than any other now known.

Index will be found on
Page 377

SUPERIOR PROJECTOR
The Standard of Excellence

For Silent and Synchronized Sound Projection

TYPE "S"
Adapted to Movietone and Vitaphone

Manufactured by

COXSACKIE HOLDING CORPORATION
COXSACKIE, N. Y., U. S. A.

INDEX

A

B

C

377

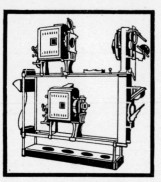

F

G

H

I

N

O

P

The Heart of Sound Reproduction

Pam 16 or 17
Price, without
tubes, $125.00

IF you have or contemplate installing any electrical reproducing device for furnishing music as an accompaniment for motion pictures, you should be vitally interested in what amplifier is used— for it is the HEART of any such equipment. Quality like the original is important—freedom from breakdowns paramount. Samson's 46 years' experience assures these as will be confirmed by Theatre Managers and most manufacturers of sound equipment. Send for illustrated bulletin TBG-1 and consult our Engineering Laboratories on special amplifier problems.

Manufacturers Since 1882

Member R. M. A.

**Main Office:-
Canton, Mass.**

**Factories:
Canton and
Watertown,
Mass.**

The American Cinematographer

The voice of the American Society of Cinematographers and the Technical magazine of the Motion Picture Industry.

THREE DOLLARS A YEAR

An Amateur Cinematography Department conducted by a professional.

An independent educational journal owned and published by the A. S. C., the Cameramasters of the Cinema World.

Publication office, Suite 1219-20-21-22, Guaranty Building, Hollywood, California, which is also headquarters of the A. S. C.

CAMERON'S BOOKS

may be obtained abroad from the following dealers

LONDON

Sidney Rentell Co., Ltd.,
93 Long Acre.

Odhams, Ltd.,
All Branches.

Kodak, Ltd.,
Kingsway.

Fountain Press, Ltd.,
14 Cliffords Inn,
Fleet Street.

American Book Co.,
86 Strand.

JAPAN

Maruzen Co., Ltd.,
16 Nihonbashi Tori-Sachome,
Tokoyo.

CHINA

Tse Chailin,
Shanghai.

MEXICO

American Photo Supply Co.,
Av. F. I. Madero 40,
Mexico City.

HONOLULU

Honolulu Photo Supply Co.,
1057 Fort Street.

IRELAND

The Camera,
2 Crow Street,
Dublin.

AUSTRALIA

Angus & Robertson, Ltd.,
89 Castlereach St.,
Sydney.

Harrington's Ltd.,
386 George St.,
Sydney.

Robertson & Mullens, Ltd.,
107 Elizabeth St.,
Melbourne.

GERMANY

Filmtechnik,
Friedrichstrasse 46,
Berlin.

INDIA

The Book Co., Ltd.,
College Square,
Calcutta.

D. B. Taraporevala Sons,
190 Hornby Road,
Bombay.

NEW ZEALAND

Whitcombe & Tombs, Ltd.,
Auckland, N. Z.

CANADA

T. Eaton Co.,
All Branches.

BUENOS AIRES

Sociedad General Cinematografica.

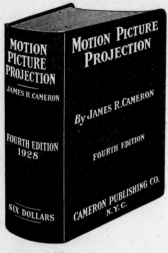